MW00655774

FIT MIND, FIT BODY

How to Achieve Your Ideal Body and Keep It FOREVER by Putting Your Motivation on Autopilot!

Created for the 95% of People
Who Struggle with Diet and Exercise

Don Staley

Published by
Brain Cell Coach, LLC
3128 Walton Blvd #122
Rochester Hills, Michigan 48309

1st Printing, 2011

ISBN: 978-0-9828993-9-7

Library of Congress Control Number: 2011913784

Staley, Don
FIT MIND, FIT BODY, How to Achieve Your Ideal Body and Keep It FOREVER by Putting Your Motivation on Autopilot!

Printed in the United States of America
Cover design Kiryl Lysenka
Book layout and design Dawn Teagarden

To Angie, Nicholas, and Reese.
You are my moon, sun, and stars.

Praise for Fit Mind, Fit Body and Don Staley

"Fit Mind, Fit Body is loaded with straight forward strategies anyone can use to overcome the failure associated with proper diet and exercise. If you are looking to utilize the power of the brain and the subconscious mind to put your fitness on autopilot this book is a must read."

—John Assaraf, San Diego, California, CEO Praxisnow.com
New York Times Bestselling Author, "The Answer" and "Having It All"

"You won't find a more creative, inspiring, and extremely giving individual as you will in Don Staley. His purpose is to impact the world in a positive way, and he does so every day. It is a breath of fresh air to see someone like him, with such a passion for serving others. Don truly intends to change the world and is doing so daily...one person or audience at a time."

—Andrew Windham, Atlanta, Georgia
Founder and CEO, www.insurancegeorgia.com

"If you are looking to be authentic and true to yourself you probably want to be fit and healthy. I've got GREAT news for you—you are SO in the right place right now! Don Staley's book Fit Mind, Fit Body will teach you exactly that and how to maintain your results for the long-term."

—Lisa Sasevich, San Diego, California
Queen of Sales Conversion, www.lisasasevich.com

"Don Staley is willing to go the extra mile so you can get whatever you dream. A lot of us don't get beyond dreaming. Don will help you achieve whatever you are looking for. It all starts with you, and Don will help you turn your dreams into action."

—Tonya Bartys, Bay City, Michigan

"Absolutely fantastic! This book is going to help you stay right on track."

—Dov Baron, Vancouver, BC, Canada
Bestselling Author, www.cycedge.com

"Don has what it takes to lead his clients through a truly positive transformation in their lives. I would highly recommend Don as your guide moving forward, regardless of where you currently are in your own personal journey."

—Todd Cole, Dallas, Texas

"Don is the gentleman one meets who immediately exudes genuine honesty and concern for others. His persistence and dedication to face challenges and meet his own worthy goals as well as to help others achieve theirs is impressive."

—Joanne Simpson, Surprise, Arizona, Life awareness coach

"If you are ready to take your game to the next level, Don Staley is the guy to help you get there."

—David J. Kramer, Cleveland, Ohio

"Don has a wonderful way of explaining concepts and has a natural gift of clear communication. He is compassionate, understanding, and inspiring. I am very grateful that he came into my life."

—Maxine Boucher, San Rafael, California

"Don is a motivator, period! He leads by example. His suggestions are easily incorporated into everyday life and they work. His enthusiasm and positive attitude are contagious."

—Natalie Haggerty, L.Ac., Sausalito, California

"I have had the opportunity to work with Don and have benefited from our time together. Many times, he has shared ideas with me to help put things into perspective that I may not have thought of on my own. He is able to 'see' things that might be 'too close' to see. He is wise, caring, and compassionate and knows his stuff. Having Don Staley in my corner is a great asset, and it gives me a great deal of confidence."

—Mercy Almquist, DeBary, Florida

"Don Staley's book Fit Mind, Fit Body is worth its weight in gold. We are shown how to thoroughly transform our mindset to finally accomplish and maintain our ideal body."

—Sheri Varela, Los Angeles, California
www.PowerUpSource.com

"Don has a way of motivating people that is rare and refreshing. Don understands the importance of consistent interaction and coaching. He easily demonstrates how to move, inspire, and motivate anyone seeking his guidance. If you are looking for someone who can truly help you transform this area of your life, Don is a wise choice for moving forward."

—Kate Phipps, Longmont, Colorado

"I've known Don for several years, now. He's not only an honest and ethical man, but he is extremely passionate about helping others reach their true potentials. Whether it is personal or professional guidance you are seeking, I would highly recommend talking to Don."

—Michael Doran, Rochester, Michigan

"Don is not only a good friend, but he's one of the most positive people I know. Scratch that! He is THE most positive person I know. We've been through a lot together, and I can definitely say that I am a better person for knowing him and spending time with him. He'll make you want to be a better person."

—Brian Kolinski, Walled Lake, Michigan

"Don is not only enthusiastic in his desire to help others achieve their goals, but he maintains the same dedication and discipline in his personal life and business. Don walks his talk and is a great model of success."

—Mindie Kniss, PhDc, Chicago, Illinois
www.knisscoaching.com

"While working with Don, I learned so much from him and his amazing insight into the Law of Attraction and the actual functions of our brains. Don is a knowledgeable individual with a gift for inspiring and teaching others. I highly recommend him, whether you are advanced in your learning or just starting on the journey."

—Lisa Rigato, Waterford, Michigan

"The minute I met Don fifteen years ago, I knew he was someone who wanted to make others feel good about themselves. Don's 'super great' attitude and devotion to inspire others make him unforgettable. What more can I say? He will always be 'Super Don' to me!"

—Audra Carney, Burton, Michigan

"Over the last twenty years, Don has been in the trenches, learning and growing. He has put that wisdom to work in his life to achieve amazing results, and now he shares these life-transforming ideas with others. These ideas can shorten your learning curve, revolutionize your habits, and ultimately change your life for the better. Don has accomplished what millions yearn for, and his desire to change the world one person at a time will catapult you to your successful destination."

—Tony Abbott, D.Ch, Barrie, Ontario, Canada
www.abbottfootclinic.ca

"He is passionate about people on a personal and professional level. Don is the kind of person you can count on to be there to support and help you in whatever you do. With his help, you'll raise your game a notch or two."

—Jordan Tenjeras, Birmingham, Michigan

"If you are looking to create new exercise habits and finally stop struggling to be consistent with exercise, then Don Staley is your man. Not only is he an inspirational leader, but he has taken the exact steps he teaches—he has 'been there, done that.' Don has 'reprogrammed' himself to achieve his goals, and he will show you how you can too. I highly recommend Don."

—Tamara Dorris, Carmichael, California
***Author,* The Communication Soul-ution**

"Don Staley is an excellent author, professional speaker, and coach. He has devoted over two decades to studying success principles—making him just that, an expert. I've enjoyed my interactions with him and wish him the very best."

—Giles Fabris, San Diego, California
www.CustomersAsRavingFans.com

"What Don Staley's book, Fit Mind, Fit Body, introduces here is the missing secret to a healthy, fit body. The valuable information within these pages can transform not only your body but your entire life. I hope all the readers realize the gold they now possess and use these principles to take action now!

—Kristi Shmyr, Edmonton, Alberta, Canada
www.goalninjas.com

"If you've tried it all and nothing has worked, then you haven't read Fit Mind, Fit Body. Get ready for an insightful breakthrough to having the results you want, and the best part is that it's not complicated. If you are truly committed in being fit, losing weight, strengthening your body, and want a vibrant and healthy lifestyle, this book is your answer.

—Joy Perreras, Boise, Idaho
www.RelaxingIntoSuccess.com

"This is a must read for anyone that has struggled with weight in the past and wants to unlock the secrets to gaining success now and forever."

—Melissa Evans, Detroit, Michigan
The Guru of Implementation, www.broshegroup.com

"Fit Mind, Fit Body is not just another fitness book or program. It lays out a new way of approaching fitness that anyone can use to change their approach to fitness and to get and stay fit for life. This book is about making easy life changes that will help you drop the extra weight and stay there effortlessly!"

—Erin Ferree, San Luis Obispo, California
www.brandstyledesign.com

"If you are looking to live a healthy life and feel great, Don has incredible wisdom to share with this book. He will teach you a proven system for getting into shape once and for all and living life to the fullest. I can definitely recommend this to anyone who wants to lose weight, or just get in shape—both physically and mentally! Don has inspired me, he'll inspire you too!"

—Karin Volo, Uppsala, Sweden
www.InspiringYourVeryBest.com

"Don began inspiring me after being in his presence for about five minutes! He is passionate about life and his work. He has worked the program and proven it works. Don lives what he talks about. Don is well read and has a wealth of knowledge, which he is anxious to share."

—Angela Major, Baton Rouge, Louisiana

"Don Staley is a passionate health advocate with a servant's heart. This book, Fit Mind, Fit Body is a MUST READ for anybody interested in regaining and maintaining optimal health."

—David Cox, D.C., Red Bluff, California

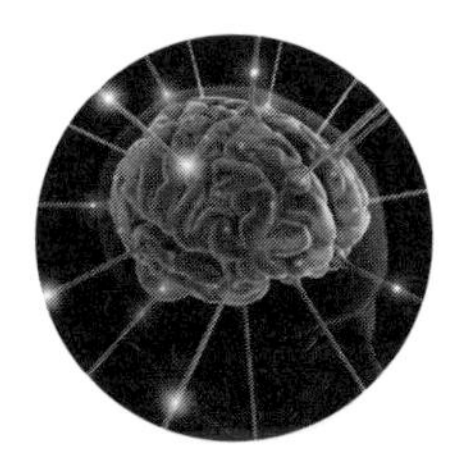

Acknowledgments

The journey to create this book began well before I sat down to write the first page. In fact, a huge mind shift had to occur before I believed I could write a book. There were many people who helped me along my path; otherwise, this project would never have been accomplished. First, I thank God—The Universe for this life in time and space—I believe that everything is from The Source. Next, I would like to thank two college teachers who had a profound effect on me: Mike LaRose, who inspired me to go into the personal development field via audio and video, and Mike Brancheau, who helped me begin to "open my eyes." Thank you for your encouragement.

I would like to thank some of my first mentors in the personal development arena: W. Clement Stone, Napoleon Hill, George Allen, Earl Nightingale, Zig Ziglar, Denis Waitley, Norman Vincent Peale, Dr. Wayne Dyer, Og Mandino, Brian Tracy, Jim Rohn, Dale Carnegie, and Anthony Robbins. I thank you for creating books, audio products, and video products. I am thankful for those of you who took your precious time to travel many miles to conduct talks for me and countless others to hear your messages. You have improved this planet beyond what we can see, and for that I am also grateful.

I wish to thank some of my more recent mentors, who were there to get me to the next level and who helped me gain certainty that not only was this book a possibility but an inevitability. My deepest thanks go to Bob Proctor, John Assaraf, Dr. Wayne Dyer, Louise L. Hay, James Ray, John DeMartini, Michael Beckwith, Fred Alan Wolf, John Hagelin, Neale Donald Walsch, Jerry Hicks, and Esther Hicks. I would also like to thank Rhonda Byrd and crew for launching the megahit film and book *The Secret.* It helped me change my life. Many thanks to William Arntz, Betsy Chasse, Mark Vicente, and crew for making the film *What the BLEEP Do We Know!?* Your film opened my eyes.

Tom Bird taught me a method for writing in a new way and gave me the hope that I could finish my book quickly. Tom, I thank you.

To all the members of the many mastermind groups who have helped hold me accountable throughout the years, I thank you. I especially want to acknowledge my friends Brian Olsen, Bill Loughead, Carletus Willis, Mike Rojas, Jennifer Michalik, Elon Bar-Evan, David J. Kramer, Rossi Saldivia, Mercy Almquist, Todd Cole, Angela Major, Natalie Haggerty, Maxine Boucher, Joanne Simpson, and Mindie Kniss. Thank you for being there. I also want to thank Lisa Sasevich and all my brothers and sisters of the "SASSY" mastermind. Your love and support has helped me complete and launch this book. I will treasure our friendship forever.

Thanks to Joanne Simpson for undertaking the monumental challenge of tweaking the first draft of this manuscript. To Christine Sommer, you put your heart into this project more than I could have ever expected anyone to do. For that zeal, I am grateful. You helped shape this book with your insights. To Angela Major, Carol Douthitt, Mercy Almquist, Andrew Windham, Dr. David Cox, Duane McGill, and Dan Gillespie, for offering your time, feedback, and encouragement early in the process, I am most grateful. Thanks to Louise Seiler, Mindy Staley, Erin Ferree, Cynthia Magg, Missy Oaks, and Sheri Varela for your help proofreading and making this book even better.

To Kiryl Lysenka for your genius, creativity, and patience during our many tweaks back and forth in our attempt to create the perfect book cover, I thank you. To Dawn Teagarden for your creative brilliance in constructing an interior design that makes this book even easier to read, I am much obliged. To Carl Levi, I thank you so very much for editing the rough edges off this book and helping me turn it into a diamond. I am grateful for you and all you have done for this book. To Dave Nelsen and Christine LePorte, thank you for polishing this diamond so it sparkles. This book will shine new light into the lives of people beyond our years. I am so grateful for you and your editing skills.

To my many wonderful friends throughout the years (you know who you are), thank you for all the fun, love, and support.

To all of my family, of which I have the immense privilege of being a part, I am truly grateful. For years, Tena Staley sent beautifully timed little notes of encouragement as well as cards and pictures to brighten my day. To you they may have been only pebbles, but to me they were giant ROCKS. I thank you. Thank you to Barb Arbuckle for making an amazingly timed phone call that was an answer to my prayer. To Robert and Roberta Sanch, Sr. (Uncle Bob and Aunt Kaye), I thank you for being examples of entrepreneurs and all the lessons of excellent customer service I learned while in your employ. Thank you for providing my first public speaking experience. To my cousin Bob (Bobby) Sanch, Jr., thank you for that conversation many years ago, which helped me begin to believe in myself, and for introducing me to the first book I ever wanted to read, which ultimately shaped my life forever. For those kindnesses, I am eternally grateful.

To my numerous nieces and nephews, I thank you for believing in me and encouraging me and for two decades of allowing me to practice teaching and inspiring others with you as my audience and students. You have taught me far more than I have taught you.

To all my brothers and sisters, Bill, Leo, Barb, Bob, Rick, Mike, John, Cheryl, and Ann and spouses, Tena, Joanna, Gord, Deb, Penny, Tim, and Dave. If life were a football game, you would be my offensive line. Thank you for the protection of your "blocking" all these years. Any touchdowns I score I owe to you.

I am especially grateful and give thanks to my parents, William A., Jr., and Elizabeth Staley who provided the loving environment in which I grew up. Thank you for being examples of what can be learned from reading books. Mom, you are a great model of love and hard work. Dad, you made many sacrifices and were the most honest man I have ever known. Dad, my only regret is that I delayed taking action for too long and you were not able to see the finished book in print before you passed from this life. I am so very appreciative that each of you taught me about love, wisdom, and integrity. I love you both.

Finally, to my best friend and wife, Angie, whose love and support made completing this project possible. I thank you for helping me with my vision and the mission of helping millions of people create their ideal lives. A special thank-you to Nicholas and Reese for giving me my "sacred space" while I let this book materialize from an idea into a manuscript and for teaching me what love really means. In your young lives, you have already taught me more than I could ever hope to teach you both if I lived one hundred years.

Table of Contents

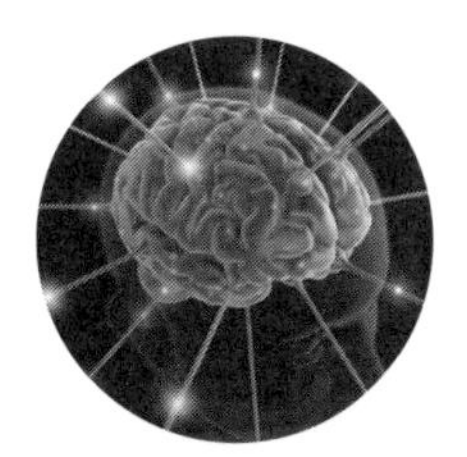

Introduction

Congratulations! You have made it through the maze of misinformation and contradictory suggestions known as the exercise, fitness, and nutritional abyss. Here, you have finally reached the solution to your past challenges of getting and staying fit and healthy. I know you have probably heard this claim before, and I can definitely appreciate the fact that you may be skeptical, but this book *is* different.

I can say that emphatically because, for over twenty years, I failed miserably at my attempts to be fit and create my ideal body. I failed at being consistent with exercise, and I ate unhealthy foods. Not only was I unfit, I was frustrated, depressed, and feeling defeated. To make matters worse, I did not know why I kept failing time after time. I had read numerous books, listened to countless audio tapes and CDs, and attended hundreds of hours of seminars and classes. Yet I still struggled and was unable to make my fitness goals stick.

When I finally was able to put all the pieces to the fitness puzzle together, my world changed forever. It took me over twenty years to develop this roadmap, and once I did, I knew I had to share it with the world. That is why I have put what I learned into this book. You can now read in a week or two what took me two decades to understand.

Not too long ago, I was struggling with many of the same challenges you may be wrestling with now. Have you ever felt as if you were banging your head against the wall because of the lack of success you kept experiencing with your exercise program? Did overcoming this seemingly impossible task of getting and staying fit seem insurmountable? It did for me.

Have you ever gotten home from work drained, and all you have energy to do is plop down on the couch and watch TV? Do you ever wish you had more motivation or discipline to exercise and eat right on a consistent basis? Have you ever had to say "no" to your children when they asked you to play because you were just too tired? I was that person just a few short years ago.

I wanted to be healthy, but I just couldn't figure out exactly what I needed to do to keep motivated and disciplined in order to be fit and energetic. I feel your pain. I know how you must feel, because I have been where you are now.

Once I learned and applied the ideas that are in this book, my life changed forever. I am now in better shape and have more energy than most people who are twenty years younger. I am now able to play comfortably with my kids and have fun doing so, while others watch in amazement.

For many people, figuring out how to eat properly and exercise on a consistent and regular basis is as complex as solving a Rubik's Cube. It doesn't have to be that way. When I figured out how to solve the fitness riddle, my entire life changed. What would you do with ten times more energy? What about unstoppable confidence?

The problem with being unfit and lethargic is not only how it affects you but how it affects everyone around you. Your kids, significant other, friends, and even your coworkers are feeling the repercussions of your unhealthy habits. What are you missing out on because you are not consistently practicing healthy habits? What will you lose if you continue on this destructive path?

We have only a limited time on this planet. Are you cutting your allotted time even shorter, or are you doing your best to extend your life? Most of the major *killers* are preventable with proper nutrition and regular exercise. By reading and applying the ideas presented here, you can add years to your life and life to your years. If your answers to many of the previous questions were not favorable, don't fret. You are not alone.

Millions of people are in the same situation. Ninety-five percent of people fail every year with their efforts to get fit. Exactly why do most people fail? They fail because they are only treating the symptom when they should be going to the cause. The symptoms will keep reappearing until you finally treat the source or cause of an ailment. Treating the cause is what this book is all about.

Today, over 61% of Americans are overweight including 33% who are obese. No pun intended, but this is a HUGE problem! Most Americans have become fat, lazy, and unhappy, and they don't know how they got into this predicament! One reason is that our habits have taken us slowly down a road we didn't even know we were traveling. No one consciously decides to be fat, lazy, unhealthy, and unhappy. We are not really looking to be in this predicament. We just appeared on this road, and here we are now, fat and unhappy.

Of course, there are some people who are "trim" but not fit. Let's assume that most people would prefer to be fit. If we are in such bad shape, how did we get here? Whose fault is it? Have you ever heard that "people are creatures of habit"? We really are. For this *out of shape* mess we are in, we can give some of the credit to our habits.

Habits live in the subconscious mind. The prefix *sub* means *below*. However, the subconscious mind is by no means less significant than the conscious mind. In fact, you will soon discover that the subconscious mind is running all of our "programs." Our subconscious mind can be likened to an operating system on a powerful computer, and our minds are unfathomably more powerful than the most sophisticated computer.

My success happened because I reprogrammed my mind. Remember, I *wanted* to, for twenty-plus years, but I couldn't get myself to do it. Unfortunately, my old conditioning consisted of habits of very little exercise and unhealthy eating. When I finally *reprogrammed* those old programs, my habits changed. Reprogramming yourself is not complicated. Anyone can do it. If you can read this book, then you too can reprogram your mind.

You might be thinking that this approach to fitness sounds too simple. Can achieving your ideal body weight really be that uncomplicated? Yes, it can. However, it is not necessarily easy. You will find that the process isn't necessarily difficult, but it will require some effort, depending on where you are presently in your personal growth path. I promise you that, when you do the work and follow the process, the effort you put in will be far outweighed by all the benefits you reap. I know this to be true and, soon, so will you!

To gain an understanding of how to create habits that will greatly empower you, you are about to embark on a great journey of discovery and ultimate fulfillment. Hopefully, it is a lifelong journey. I did my best to give you all the information I have learned to help you help yourself get where you are yearning to go. I said "help you help yourself," because it is really *you* who will change your life. You can do it, and I will be along to guide you!

What You Will Find in This Book

This book comprises eighteen chapters, which fit into five sections. Briefly, I'd like to introduce each section and then each chapter to you. The first of the five sections is the foundation, which gives you a base from which to build as you proceed through the book. **It is important that you read the**

"Foundation" section first. Avoid the urge to jump into the "how to" material, because a solid foundation must be built first to create a strong structure that will endure.

The second section is the "Creation or Initiation Process," which shows you how to create your ideal body. The "Retraining Process" is the next section, and it shows you how to *reset* your fitness thermostat to your ideal body. Fourth, the "Facilitation" section guides you with a system to speed up your progress and also keeps you going. Finally, the last section is all about "Implementation." This is your action plan, and this section gives you a day-by-day plan to put all you have learned into practice, so you can reap the results you desire once and for all.

Next, I would like to briefly introduce you to each of the eighteen chapters.

In chapter 1, you will begin to think differently about your health practices (eating and exercising). You will come to understand that most of your behaviors are habits, how powerful habits are, and how to change them.

In chapter 2, you will learn about the brain and how it is one of the main reasons for our success or failure. In particular, knowing about a few different parts of the brain and what they do will give you an understanding of what is happening in your brain and body when you are changing your behavior or stepping outside of your comfort zone.

In chapter 3, we venture deeper than the brain, into the subconscious mind. This chapter supports and provides the *whys* for the reprogramming process and why reprogramming works. In this chapter, you will gain a visual of what the mind *looks* like, and you will learn what processes the subconscious mind runs.

Chapter 4 discusses the Great Law and other Laws of the Universe and how they tie into our success or lack of it. Knowing these laws will greatly improve your results. If you don't know the rules to the game, how can you play to win?

Chapter 5 reminds you that *you* are completely responsible for the results you experience. Taking personal responsibility is the key to open up the padlock of success. If you don't take personal responsibility for your thoughts and actions and, ultimately, for your success or failure, you may be doomed forever to your present conditions—plus or minus a few minor changes. Everyone on the planet has longed for the fruit that is yielded from the tree of taking responsibility. This chapter reveals that effect.

Chapter 6 details the importance of knowing what your desire is and making sure it is not merely a wish or a hope. It must be a strong desire. If you intend to achieve your objective, your desire must be strong enough for you to hold your thoughts on it until your new programming takes hold. What is it you truly want? Is it a red hot desire or merely a wish?

Chapter 7 covers the next step in the process. To attain a crystal clear idea or mental picture of exactly what it is you truly want, you need a clear vision so that you will avoid being easily distracted and run off course. You will also learn about finding an ideal body photo and what to do with it.

Chapter 8 is about making a decision to achieve your desire. To know your desire is one thing; deciding to go after it is another. To make a decision is to *cut off* all other possibilities. The second part is about making a decision on what time frame are you committed to.

In chapter 9, you will learn how your beliefs control your actions, but, more importantly, you can learn how to change your beliefs through repetition if they are not serving you.

Chapter 10 is about how commitment is an essential element of the components needed to achieve your goal. In this chapter, you will learn that you MUST commit to your new vision and to the process of reconditioning yourself to acquire the new habits necessary to accomplish these new goals. If you are not committed to your goal long enough to create new habits, you will revert back to your previous conditioning or programming. If you don't commit, you won't do what is necessary to achieve the level of accomplishment that you want. We need to do the work. For example, carrying gym cards in our wallets won't make us fit unless we are committed to get to the gym and use them.

Chapter 11 will show you the two most important types of actions you must take to achieve your ideal body. If you neglect these two actions, most likely you will find yourself among the 95% who fail to maintain long-term success. Chapter 11 is about taking action.

Chapter 12 deals with the actual four-pronged approach to reconditioning of your subconscious mind in order to move to the next level. This is the same approach I have used to create daily exercise habits and good eating habits. The object of this chapter is to show you how to recondition old beliefs and habits, which are moving you away from your goal, and turn them into what you need to achieve your ideal body and ideal life.

In chapter 13, you will learn the two major categories of accountability: internal and external. Within these categories, there are dozens of methods of accountability that not only increase the likelihood of success but also shorten the time it takes to achieve your ideal body. This chapter presents you with many ideas on how to use accountability to help facilitate your success.

Chapter 14 presents you with another key way to help your progress by being grateful and expressing gratitude for everything you do. This concept helps you appreciate where you have been and where you are going. You will learn to appreciate both your successes and your failures and why that is important.

In chapter 15, you will learn one of the biggest lessons a baby can teach. You will also learn the importance of giving yourself pats on the back, especially when altering your behavior. In addition, you will learn to celebrate your failures as well as your successes.

Chapter 16 shows you how to become more aware of your environment. This awareness is critical to facilitating your success.

Chapter 17 talks about the need to constantly increase your understanding. This chapter will present you with multiple methods to do so.

Finally, in chapter 18, which is one of *most critical* chapters, we examine your taking action. To help you in that process, this chapter IS your *action plan*. Regardless of how good or helpful all of the preceding information is, if you neglect to *apply* those ideas, you will limit your opportunity to gain excellent results.

The purpose of this book is to help you obtain your ideal fit and healthy body. Application is critical. In this last chapter, I help you apply these ideas with a step-by-step, day-by-day approach. There should be no confusion of what you are to do. **Just follow the steps.**

How can you benefit the most from this book? To read a book once is a great start. I encourage you to read it at least *three times*. **In fact, don't just read this book—study it!**

On the first reading, you will lay the foundation and familiarize yourself with the concepts. On the second run-through, I suggest implementing—taking action! After you have moved forward through the process, reread it to make sure you remain on track and are performing your assignments correctly. Finally, I recommend you come back to this book at least once a year to refresh yourself and keep inspired.

Another powerful way you can benefit from this information is to buy a few extra copies and pass them out to your friends—or you can strongly encourage your friends to buy copies of their own. Then, you all can go through this set of experiences together as a mastermind group (chapter 13). Your exposing your friends to this book may change their lives, and, for some, it could save their lives.

This book has shown up for you at this exact time because you wanted or needed it. What is interesting, and you may not understand this yet, is *you attracted this book to yourself* at this exact time. You are the cause. You are the one who brought this book into your life. **Your desire is ready to unfold. You are the only one who can unfold it.** There is only one you, and there is only one now. You have it *now*, so let's begin!

Don Staley

P.S. I welcome interaction with my readers. Therefore, you may contact me by e-mail or postal mail or through my website.

Website: http://www.donstaley.com/fitmindbook

E-mail: don@donstaley.com

Address:
Don Staley
3128 Walton Blvd #122
Rochester Hills, MI 48309

"Our deepest fear is not that we are inadequate.

Our deepest fear is that we are powerful beyond measure.

It is our light, not our darkness that most frightens us.

We ask ourselves, Who am I to be brilliant,
gorgeous, talented, fabulous?

Actually, who are you not to be? You are a child of God.

Your playing small does not serve the world.

There is nothing enlightened about shrinking so that other
people won't feel insecure around you.

We are all meant to shine, as children do.

We were born to make manifest the glory of God
that is within us.

It's not just in some of us; it's in everyone.

And as we let our own light shine, we unconsciously give other
people permission to do the same.

As we are liberated from our own fear, our presence
automatically liberates others."

—Marianne Williamson, from **A Return to Love**

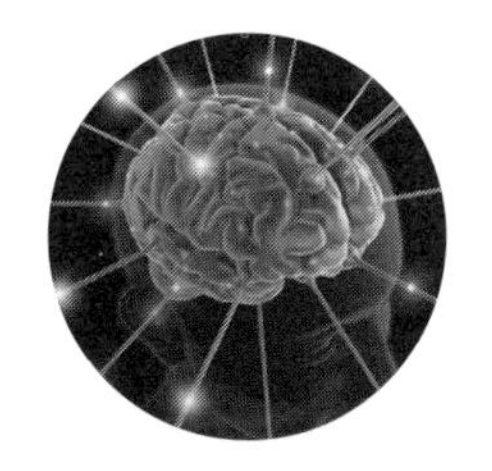

CHAPTER 1

The Power Of Habits

"Habits are at first cobwebs, then cables."

—Spanish proverb

Our bodies are remarkable and will tolerate amazing challenges. Can you imagine dumping a Coca-Cola into your car's gas tank? What about stuffing French fries into your computer's disk drive? It sounds ridiculous, doesn't it? Perhaps your car cost you tens of thousands of dollars, or maybe its price was only a few thousand dollars. Most likely, your computer cost less than $2,000. Regardless, you would not treat your vehicle or your computer in such a destructive way. If you did so, most people would accuse you of being crazy.

What if you owned a luxury car, such as a Cadillac or a BMW, and it cost $50,000 to $100,000? Would you take even better care of it than you would a cheaper one? How are you taking care of your billion-dollar body? Would you consider stuffing French fries and a greasy cheeseburger into your gas tank frequently and still expect it to perform at optimal levels?

I am not saying that eating French fries once in a while is wrong, because your body is so amazing that it can deal with small amounts of toxins. However, if you were to eat them every day, it wouldn't be long before you would notice severe ramifications. Remember the old saying by Mark Twain, "ALL things in moderation, including moderation"? If we were to stuff some fries and a cheeseburger into your car's gas tank, wash them down with a Coke, and then start your car and began to drive it down the road, it would not be long before we would face the negative consequences of our actions.

Upon experiencing the results, it would be unlikely that we would treat our car like that ever again. We are blessed and challenged with bodies that can take on many trials, but they have their limits.

We can dump the same useless, empty food into our bodies and we may or may not get upset stomachs. However, if we keep abusing our bodies, chances are they will stall on us.

Generally, we won't see the ramifications of our poor choices for a long time, so there is no *obvious* connection between the behavior of eating poorly and inactivity (cause) and the result of low energy and poor health (effect).

We Are Creatures of Habit

The problem is that most of us habitually eat junk food. Also, we don't move our bodies enough. We are couch potatoes, who lack consistent exercise.

You may be thinking, "Are you telling me that I can't have a cheeseburger?"

No, what I'm saying is, pay attention to what you are doing. Ask yourself, "Why did I eat this food? Was it due to a habit, or did I consciously choose to eat this food?"

From the way many of us have been conditioned over the years, most people would think we were crazy if we treated our automobiles the way we treat our bodies. We dump junk into our bodies, but we would never do that to our cars.

It is our conditioning that has us on autopilot, so we mindlessly proceed by eating carelessly and remaining inactive. Over many years, this paradigm has become the norm. Look where it has taken us as a society—to a level of obesity unknown decades ago.

Usually, from the moment they wake in the morning to the instant they fall asleep, most people appear to be operating on autopilot. They are not really thinking about what they are doing. They just keep perpetuating their habits.

Have you ever set a New Year's resolution? Have you made the same resolutions year after year? I know I have. With some focus and determination, this year *can* be different. It *will* be different for me and for many others who have finally learned why resolutions do not work. Now, it can be different for you, too.

Are you curious? The purpose of this book is to show you how to take the actions you wish to take and to stop acting in ways that no longer serve you. When you master this concept, you can really begin enjoying life to the fullest.

> "Bad habits are like a comfortable bed—
> easy to get into, but hard to get out of."
>
> **—unknown author**

Earlier, I mentioned the old adage that people are creatures of habit. This is true. We *are* creatures of our habits! Also, you may have heard that habits are difficult to break or that you cannot teach an old dog new tricks. While the first part of the last sentence can be partly true—habits *can* be somewhat challenging to break—the second part is false. The reality is that you *can* teach an old dog new tricks—if you know how.

What Is a Habit?

A habit is an acquired pattern of behavior that often occurs automatically. People may think habits are actions, such as biting your fingernails, overeating, or smoking. However, habits can also be thoughts, e.g., "I am hungry," "I need a smoke," "I'm not good enough," "I CAN'T do this" and "I can do this" or "I am a success." If you repeatedly think a certain thought without much effort, that is a habit. A habit can be a powerful ally to have on your side.

We Can Change

Have you ever looked at your wrist to see what time it was and realized you were not wearing your watch? I think we all have done that. Taking it a step further, I purposefully alternate the wrist on which I wear my watch. I wear it on the right wrist for a while (approximately thirty days) and then switch and wear it on the left wrist for a while. By following this practice, I am reminded of the power of habits.

If you feel adventuresome, give it a whirl sometime. You will be amazed at how many times you look to the wrist you had formed the habit of looking at only to find that wrist bare. Obviously, you formed the small habit of looking at a certain wrist. The point is to understand that there are many things we do without conscious thought. We call these actions habits. My intention is to keep myself aware that there are many habits running. As a result, I am helped to remember to put more conscious thought into areas where I want to improve.

Why Are Habits So Powerful?

To understand the power of habits, let's go a bit deeper to appreciate the science or biology that explains what a habit is. We will talk a lot about the brain and the neural net (group of brain cells). For now, let's jump back into the biology of the brain. There are literally hundreds of billions of brain cells with trillions of possible connections. Many scientists estimate that there are **more possible connections in the human brain than there are stars in the universe!** You can think of it as having the worldwide telephone network completely situated in a human brain. Each cell has the potential to be connected to any cell in the brain. This is how the brain thinks. A thought is sent from neuron to neuron. The more a thought is *practiced*, the easier it is for that same thought to be thought again.

> "Neurons that fire together, wire together."
>
> **—Donald Hebb**

Thought travels the path of least resistance. Perhaps you have heard a similar statement regarding water. Water also takes the path of least resistance, and so does electricity. The brain is basically an electrical (and chemical) switching station, and it also takes the path of least resistance. The essence of a habit boils down to the fact that it is easier for the brain to operate using the same pathways. This is why the old saying is so true, that once you have the habit, the habit has you.

Habits Can Be Bad or Good

Habits are not necessarily bad. Some habits are good. When you refer to the Laws of the Universe, a habit is neither bad nor good. It is both and it is neither. It depends on what you relate it to and what you decide it is. This is the Law of Relativity, which we'll talk more about later. In this case, it depends on what that habit is and whether it moves you closer to your goal or *ideal* life or moves you further away. When you are uncovering certain habits in your life, a good question to ask yourself is "Is this moving me closer to my goal or further away?" Generally speaking, if the habit in question is NOT moving you closer to your goal, it is moving you further away and is a habit you'll want to replace.

Are We Forever Trapped by Our Habits?

We are creatures of habit. Does that mean we are trapped forever in our habits of doom? No! We created the habits, sometimes with the help of others, and we can rid ourselves of those nasty habits and replace them with good, productive, life-enhancing habits. Neuro-plasticity (flexibility or ability to move/change) enables the brain—and, thus, habits—to change.

> "A nail is driven out by another nail. Habit is overcome by habit."
>
> **—Desiderius Erasmus**

Based on the latest brain research, which states we are not hard-wired, we now know we can change. Neuro-plasticity or brain plasticity indicates that our brains are "plastic" or moveable—meaning we can change thought patterns and even the very position of the neural net inside the brain. Neuro-plasticity or brain plasticity refers to the changes that occur in the organization of the brain. Norman Doidge, a psychiatrist, said neuro-plasticity is "one of the most extraordinary discoveries of the twentieth century."

How Do We Change Our Habits?

The first step to changing a habit is realizing you have acquired a habit that is not serving you. In the next step, you must desire to eliminate or replace it. That concept is essential—you must replace bad habits with good habits. For instance, if you possess a habit of not exercising and you desire to get and stay fit, you simply replace the lack of exercising with a habit of exercising every day. Eventually, your habit *becomes* exercising every day. By adding this new pattern of behavior (in this case, exercising), you have automatically eliminated the old pattern of behavior (habit) of not exercising. Another example is if someone overeats. The bad habit is overeating. The challenge of this behavior (habit) of overeating is to replace it with a habit of eating in moderation.

This approach can be used for any habit you want to implement and replace. I will be the first to admit that this is easier said than done, but it can be accomplished when you want (desire) to change strongly enough. We have all replaced habits before; how do you think you acquired your bad habits in the first place? Although it may appear that bad habits just happen, a behavior must be practiced enough times before it becomes a habit. Later, I will cover the exact steps to take to create new habits. Once you have a new understanding and apply the steps we are talking about, you too can create better habits, while replacing the habits that no longer serve you.

Habits Are Our Autopilot

Have you ever driven your car home or to somewhere very familiar while conversing intently with someone? Maybe you were talking on the phone, or maybe the person was sitting right next to you as you drove. After chatting away for what seemed like a short time, the next thing you know, you arrive at your destination. Surprisingly, you might not remember how you traveled there. Has this ever happened to you? I must confess it has happened to me. As the conversation held your conscious attention, your subconscious mind *held* the steering wheel. Because you have driven to this destination many times, you created a habit or a *program* (like a computer program) to drive that particular route. While your conscious mind was distracted by the conversation, your subconscious mind essentially "took the wheel." You drove on autopilot based on a "habit" of driving to that destination.

You might think, "This is a nice example, but what does it mean to me?" It means that once you form a habit of the behavior you desire to incorporate into your life, it becomes a lot easier to maintain that behavior in the long run. **If you want to eat nutritious foods and exercise regularly, all you have to do is make those goals into habits.**

If you want to eat nutritious foods and exercise regularly, all you have to do is make those goals into habits.

Habits are powerful and great allies to have on your side. You know how challenging it is to work against habits. It is *now* time to work *with* them. You can employ the habit of reprogramming to help form other habits of behaviors you now choose to implement into your new, ideal life.

Our bodies—and in particular, our brains—are very powerful and complex. In fact, we are constantly learning more about both on a regular basis. The brain is the control center. Once we understand how to use it, the process of accomplishing our goals becomes more simplified and many of our present challenges can become accomplishments.

We will always have challenges. If we didn't, we would be six feet under. Challenges are good. They provide the resistance for us to grow. To help us better understand the brain and especially our mind (the subconscious and the conscious) the next chapter will give you a basic understanding, which will allow you to move through the rest of the process to create your ideal body and your ideal life.

The Critical Habit That Can Change Your Life

Chances are, you currently don't have a daily practice of consciously reprogramming your subconscious mind. If you do, congratulations! Keep reading and you may get some additional ideas to help you along your path. For most people reading this book for the first time, the **reprogramming process** is not yet a daily habit. The first thing we need to do is establish a habit of reprogramming the "re-programmer" (you).

When you begin to change a habit and you don't have the habit of reprogramming yourself incorporated into your repertoire of habits, you may not stick to the process. This is because the process of reprogramming requires a certain behavior in and of itself. It requires time and consistency to develop that habit, too. If we don't stick to the process, then all may be lost, and then you will doubt the validity of this program.

I believe this is where most self-help and personal development books drop the ball. Their intentions are good. They tell you what to do, and then they expect you to do it. If it's a new habit, and you don't know how to create a new habit or your desire is less than intense, you will only persevere for a short time, and, most likely, you will then revert to your previous habits.

It has been my experience that the reason most people ultimately fail with a personal development program is that they don't take the time to install a habit to recondition themselves. A new habit needs to be created, and that habit is the **reprogramming of the subconscious mind to create new habits**. You might be asking yourself, "What comes first, the chicken or the egg?" With this new understanding, you can use your *will* for a period of time to create this new habit of reprogramming. Then, you can incorporate the same process to create the habits that will bring you to your goals.

Initially, it is a two-step process. You will be creating two habits. One is the habit of the process of reconditioning yourself, which is the habit of reconditioning old beliefs into new habits. Second is the actual habit you are striving to implement in your life.

When you begin something new, it is not yet a habit. When someone reads a book and the book tells him or her to do certain things for a period of time, that action is a *behavior* that needs to be done in order to accomplish things.

This new behavior or action may be a challenge to do consistently if it is not yet a habit. It will require your will, focus, commitment, and a certain amount of effort. However, no matter how good the advice is, if you don't take that action long enough to create a habit, you will revert back to your old behaviors. Unless your desire is extremely strong, there is a high probability that you won't continue to do that action consistently every day until a conciously created habit is formed (incubation stage).

When we begin, we will be incorporating this seemingly small and critical detail of **creating the habit of the process of reconditioning** until you have established a solid habit of the mental reconditioning process. Thirty days is a start. It can actually take a minimum of ninety days, every day. Perhaps 180 days is most realistic. If you are intending to create a habit to make a certain behavior be as automatic as breathing for the rest of your life, you are planning lifestyle changes, aren't you? In that case, what is 180 days? Isn't it a flash in the pan compared to your lifetime?

My intention is for you to live a good, long, healthy, and fun life. Hopefully, that is also your intention. To begin the process, we will strive for thirty days, which is very obtainable. You will later target sixty, ninety, 120, and then 180 days. To drive this new habit foundation home, we ultimately will strive for five hundred days in a row. Can you keep a new behavior going for five hundred consecutive days? Of course you can. If I can, you can. It is a matter of having a strong desire and reconditioning yourself to form new habits. Then, you must commit in order to achieve your goals. You will be taking action until your desire becomes reality and then tweaking those actions, as necessary, along the way.

What Is Your Ultimate Habit?

Your ultimate habit is the habit or action you now choose to commit to on a regular basis. This is the action that makes your goal materialize. Once you have the habit of reprogramming incorporated into your daily regimen, then you can consciously create your new habit. You do this by simply taking that action over and over on a consistent basis. When done in conjunction with the reprogramming process, this added course of action is facilitated much more easily.

Remember how easily an airplane flies on autopilot? Once you have a habit of reprogramming yourself, your goal habits will be much easier to implement. For each new habit you intend to create, you will reprogram your subconscious mind to believe that taking that action is normal and that you already do it. Teach your mind, and your body will follow.

> "Ninety-nine hundredths or, possibly, nine hundred and ninety-nine thousandths of our activity is purely automatic and habitual, from our rising in the morning to our lying down each night."

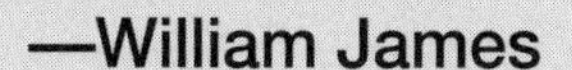

—William James

TEACHING POINTS

- ☑ Most people run on autopilot without thinking about their actions.
- ☑ Habits are powerful because they are based in the subconscious mind.
- ☑ We are creatures of habit.
- ☑ Habits are behaviors (or actions) practiced or repeated frequently.
- ☑ We can change by **replacing defective habits with effective habits.**
- ☑ You change or replace a habit by consistently practicing the action or behavior of the new habit.
- ☑ There are two types of habits to create: the critical habit—reprogramming yourself taking action(s).

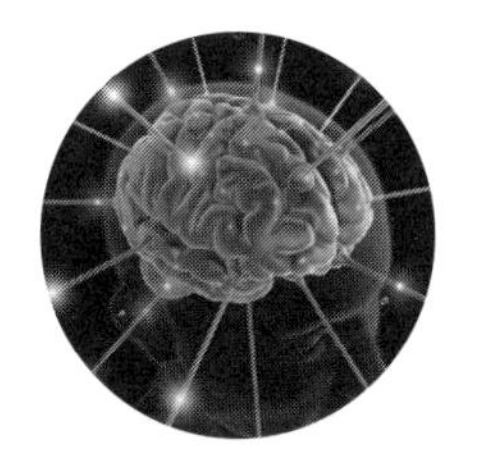

CHAPTER 2

The All-Powerful Human Brain

"Don't let your brain interfere with your heart."

—Albert Einstein

Biology 101...The Brain

Let us refresh our biology knowledge, starting with the brain. The brain is our computer, and it runs the show, as far as our physical body is concerned. We have a conscious mind and a subconscious mind. The conscious mind has several functions. Since we were babies, we were being *programmed.* Unfortunately, the people *programming* us did not necessarily know what they were doing. In fact, most of our parents, families, teachers, and religious leaders didn't know they were people programmers. They may have known it to a point, but what we are talking about today wasn't really thought about much, if at all, back then.

Your brain is an amazing and powerful instrument that can either serve or hinder you, depending on the programming or conditioning it has received. In the first part of our lives, as kids, we really didn't have much say about what type of programming we received. In fact, it is likely that we had no idea of the concept. Now, as adults, it is time to take responsibility and make the necessary repairs to our "mental boat." Some of us are taking on water and getting tired of bailing. Hold on. We are going to talk about repairing some of those holes, which will make the bailing easier and more effective.

Biology 102... Brain Cells, One Hundred Billion Strong!

Back to the brain. The human brain is made up of approximately one hundred billion cells, with another one million support cells. There are over one hundred trillion dendrite spinal protuberance (DSP) connections. DSP connections are highly complex branching structures that connect the brain cells to one another. We have the complexity of the world's telephone system in one cell. Multiply that by one hundred billion. Wow! You might want to read the last few sentences again.

We can *call* anywhere in the brain to any memory or thought. Our prior thoughts and memories are stored in these cells, and they act like little mini video clips of our past thoughts. When we think a certain thought, it replays the video via the neural net of cells we have. The more we think a certain thought, the more that pathway is connected or linked, making it easier to go down that pathway again. Eventually, after a number of thought repetitions, it becomes the path of least resistance.

Although there are many parts of the brain, you don't need to be a neural scientist to master your life. I am not a neural scientist, but I do have a passion to learn about the brain and how it affects performance. In my opinion, the more you know about the brain and how it relates to performance, controlling behavior, and habits, the more you increase your understanding. The more you understand, the more elegantly you can ease through life.

What really made an impact on me and my success was understanding a few different areas and functions of the brain. The human brain is unfathomably complex. Countless volumes have been written about it, and I am sure many more will be written as we continue to learn more about it. The real *last frontier* is the brain and, in particular, the mind. The mind and the brain are not the same, although the brain is a part of the mind. The brain is the hardware and the mind is the software. The mind is the activity.

We were each born with a conscious and subconscious mind. They are both critical to survival. What most people forget or don't understand is that the subconscious mind controls our long-term behaviors and habits. Approximately 87% of the brain's mass is dedicated to the subconscious mind. That means only 13% of the mass of the brain is working on our conscious thoughts and desires. If we consider the conscious and subconscious minds as part of a team, and we delegate an assignment to one part of the team, which part would you want working on the project? When I am working on an undertaking that I can delegate, it makes sense to me to have the powerhouse part of the team work on it.

A desire or idea resides in the conscious mind, and the results materialize from the subconscious mind. The conscious mind is for setting goals; the subconscious mind is for achieving them. We will go into greater depth in the chapter on reprogramming. However, in this chapter, we are talking about certain things you may experience during the process of reprogramming in order to help you better understand that process.

Therefore, when you step out of your comfort zone and things that impede your progress start happening, you will understand and take action despite the appearances. You won't panic and revert back to safety and your old behaviors. Knowing that these obstacles are the result of going beyond the terror barrier will help facilitate change to improve your life.

> "What is necessary to change a person is to change his awareness of himself."
>
> —Abraham Maslow

Knowing These Three Amigos Helped Change My Life

The likelihood of succeeding increases by being familiar with the reticular activating system (RAS), hypothalamus, and amygdala (the three amigos), which are a part of the psycho-cybernetic mechanism. I am not a scientist or a medical professional, so I intend to highlight a few general ideas and not delve too deeply into details. I believe that it is not necessary to grasp every element or component but to possess a basic understanding of these areas to be aware of why we take certain actions and why we might fail to take other actions.

The RAS—Reticular Activating System

The RAS, or reticular activating system, is a filter and can be likened to your own personal Google search engine. The RAS is made up of a group of cells in the back of the brain that operate eight hundred times faster than normal brain cells. These cells, or neurons, filter out everything not on our *important* list. Every second, millions of bits of information bombard us, but we are only consciously aware of about two thousand bits. The RAS lets in only information on our *important* list, and we decide what is on that list. This is done both consciously and unconsciously. Have you ever bought a new car, and then, all of a sudden, you noticed that same car everywhere you went? That is your RAS at work.

The RAS filters information from the conscious mind to the subconscious mind and vice versa. It is necessary to understand that we don't see many of the things around us because our minds are filtering them out. We see with our brains, not our eyes.

Presently, there may be things right in front of you that could aid you in the accomplishment of your goals. However, if your current programming will not let that information in, you will not see these opportunities. If an overweight program is running in your subconscious mind, when useful fitness information or ideas present themselves, you will not pick them up until that program is replaced or dissolved. When we put the reprogramming to work along with the understanding of the RAS, we essentially direct our RAS to notify us whenever it picks up something that can help us to achieve the new goal of developing our ideal body.

"We see with our eyes, but we observe with our minds."

—Don Staley

The Hypothalamus

The hypothalamus is a part of the brain responsible for sensory information. The hypothalamus is a human mini-chemical factory. It produces chemicals, or hormones (small-chain amino acids), for every emotion we have. There are hormones for sex, love, hate, depression, hope, and frustration, etc. If there is an emotion you can feel in the body, there is a hormone related to it.

In the film *What the BLEEP Do We Know!?*, Dr. Joe Dispenza describes the process, and the movie does a great job illustrating it. If you haven't seen the movie, I recommend it. If you are feeling an emotion, it is actually a hormone created by the hypothalamus or other parts of the brain and body. When I understood that, it changed my life. It is easier to control emotions when you know your brain and body are manufacturing the chemicals we *feel* as emotions.

The Amygdala

The amygdala is the part in the brain known as the emotion center. It is responsible for the release of our emotions. The first priority of the brain is the preservation of life. The next major function of the brain is to make sure our outside world matches our inside world. What we believe on the inside must mirror what we see on the outside. Homeostasis, also known as the state of equilibrium, is our comfort zone. **When we step out of our comfort zone, the amygdala sends signals to release chemicals throughout the brain and the body. These chemicals bring us back to safety.**

When we step out of our comfort zone, the amygdala sends signals to release chemicals throughout the brain and the body. These chemicals bring us back to safety.

This concept is important, because when you change a behavior or create a new habit, you encounter some chemical resistance, such as those manifested in doubt, fear, and anxiety. That resistance issued by the body is normal and can help you achieve your goals when you become aware of it. It is OK to overcome or work through the resistance. **When you step outside of your comfort zone, the amygdala kicks in and you experience feelings, which are signals to retreat back to safety (your old habits).** Are these things making more sense now?

We Have a Mental Thermostat

Maxwell Maltz, in his book *Psycho-Cybernetics*, tells us that the brain and nervous system are parts of a cybernetic mechanism. Cybernetics, as defined by Webster's *New World Dictionary*, published 2002, is a comparative study of human control systems, such as the brain and complex electronic systems. The word "cybernetics" comes from the Greek word ***kybernan,*** which means **to steer**.

We all possess this psycho-cybernetic mechanism. We can either use it to our advantage by giving it a clear mental picture toward which to steer, or we can fail to use it to our advantage by not being clear on the mental picture we are striving to achieve. We can also give it a negative image or a picture of what we don't want. Either way, this mechanism is functioning, and it is up to each one of us to decide what we want our psycho-cybernetic mechanism to work toward.

Cybernetic Mechanism

A great example of a cybernetic mechanism is a thermostat in your house. Your house thermostat is set to accommodate your comfort level, depending on the season and climate. Its purpose is to keep you comfortable. When it gets hot outside and your house heats up, the thermostat recognizes the deviation in temperature, an electrical signal is sent to the air conditioning unit, and the air turns on. This system eventually brings the temperature in the house back to your preset comfort zone.

When the temperature reaches the comfort zone, the air shuts off. The same is true in the winter, when it gets cold. As the house temperature becomes cold, the thermostat recognizes the deviation in temperature, and an electrical signal is sent to the furnace. The furnace turns on and eventually brings the temperature in the house back into the comfort zone you had programmed or preset. When the temperature reaches the comfort zone, the furnace shuts off.

Temporary Fixes Are Only That—Temporary

A few years ago, in our home, I installed a new programmable thermostat, which is designed to operate more efficiently. One of the benefits of this type of programmable device is that we can set the temperatures for certain days of the week and for certain time blocks. Everything was going great when it was first installed because I was the only one who knew how to reprogram it. I set it for a happy medium temperature, which was intended to keep everyone happy. Of course, this situation wasn't good enough for my wife. Once she learned how to reprogram it, she started messing with the settings to make it hotter in the winter and colder in the summer.

Before she learned how to reprogram it, she would temporarily adjust it by manually moving the temperature setting. This action altered the temperature temporarily and quite quickly, so she was happy—at least for a short while. Once the time for the next time block setting was reached, the thermostat reverted back to my programmed setting for that time block. Obviously, this wasn't to her liking, so she would have to exert additional effort again to attain her goal of a certain temperature.

My wife's manual effort did work temporarily, but eventually it would **ALWAYS REVERT** back to the initial programming. After wrestling with this challenge for a while, she realized it would be far less work to take some time to learn how to reprogram it. It wasn't that complex. The instructions were right on the inside cover all along. Once she reprogrammed the thermostat, it maintained the temperature she liked and reduced irritation and frustration, at least for my wife.

It didn't matter if either one of us liked the result or not. The system produced a result based on the current program installed, and it would keep producing those results until it was reprogrammed. Sure, it could be temporarily altered, but, irrefutably, it would revert back to the set program.

This is exactly what happens in many areas of your life, although you don't possess such an obvious thermostat or gauge to see what the programming is set to. Your psycho-cybernetic mechanism operates the same way. Whatever your mental or subconscious programming is, that is the comfort zone of your mental thermostat. Accordingly, each of us has a mental thermostat for every area of our lives.

If your programming says you are overweight or out of shape and then you start getting into shape, the mental thermostat will engage, signaling you to go back to your comfort zone. In my opinion, 95% of all diet and exercise programs fail because of this reason. When we start making progress, our bodies signal us to go back to safety. Most people, and I was guilty as well, do what my wife did—a temporary fix. They either do not know how to reprogram themselves or think it is too much work. Therefore, most people make manual (temporary) adjustments (trying the latest diet or exercise program), and, before they know it, they are right back where they started or worse. They may even be further back because they may have added a few extra pounds.

Understanding that our brain has a cybernetic mechanism whose job is to keep us comfortable helped me understand what happened to me in the past every time I started to get in shape. My brain realized I was stepping out of my comfort zone, and it started sending my body chemicals to alert me to go back to safety. Finally, I realized I *could step forward*, knowing that these feelings originated because of my amygdala and psycho-cybernetic mechanism's trying to send me back to homeostasis.

> "You will either step forward into growth, or you will step backward into safety."
>
> **—Abraham Maslow**

Abraham Maslow said that at any given moment we have two options. "You will either step forward into growth, or you will step backward into safety." Our body will *feel* as though we should step back into safety (our comfort zone) because the brain and other parts of the body just released chemicals. However, **every time we step forward into growth, we E X P A N D our comfort zone and, thus, reprogram our minds with a new program**. This is one of the fastest ways to advancement. You must expand your comfort zone. The good news is that now it will be easier, because you know what is happening with your body when you reach the *terror barrier*, as my mentor Bob Proctor calls it. The next time you are making progress and you feel as though you need to retreat, realize you are crossing the *terror barrier* and your brain is attempting to keep you safe.

More than likely, you have heard the old saying "As a man thinketh in his heart, so is he." Whatever we truly believe inside our being is what we will become.

"Your conscious mind doesn't resist change. It's your subconscious programming or conditioning that resists change."

—Don Staley

TEACHING POINTS

- ☑ We have a chemical, or hormone, for every emotion we experience.
- ☑ Get to know your three new amigos of the brain: RAS (reticular activating system), hypothalamus, and the amygdala.
- ☑ The conscious mind is for setting goals, and the subconscious mind is for achieving them.
- ☑ When you step out of your comfort zone, it is normal to feel doubt, fear, and anxiety.
- ☑ The only way to advance is to step forward into growth.
- ☑ We have a mental thermostat known as a cybernetic mechanism.

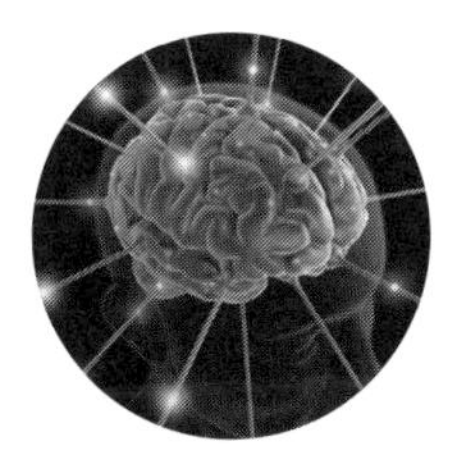

CHAPTER 3

The Subconscious Mind and Behavior

> "The mind is the limit. As long as the mind can envision the fact that you can do something, you can do it—as long as you really believe 100%."
>
> **—Arnold Schwarzenegger**

Get a Picture of Your Mind

One of the best visuals that helped me get a handle on the mind was a diagram I first learned about from Bob Proctor in 1996. It took some time for that message to germinate in the soil of my mind. When I saw this idea again ten years later, it finally took root. Regardless of where this image came from, it has tremendous potential power when you take time to absorb it into *your* mind. What we are doing with affirmations, visualizations, meditations, and mental martial arts is to replace old ideas with new ideas within the subconscious mind.

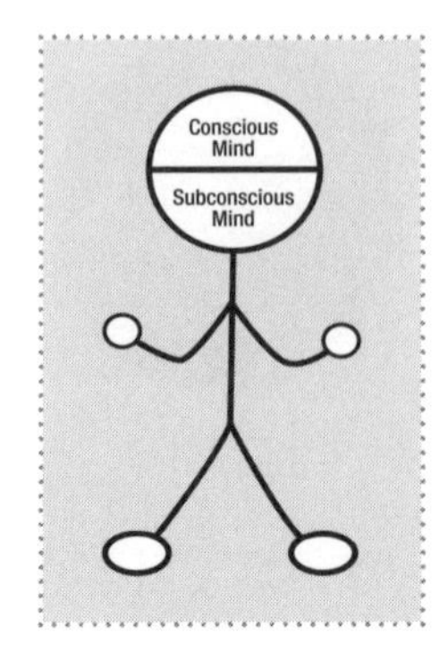

In the second diagram, we see four stick people. The circle is the head, which is divided into a top half and a bottom half. The top half represents the conscious mind, which accounts for a small fraction of our potential power. The bottom half is the subconscious, which represents about 90%–95% of the causes of all our actions, behaviors, and habits. In the first stick person, you will notice that the "Y" is in both the top and bottom portions of the *mind* (conscious and subconscious), so there is harmony—both ideas are the same.

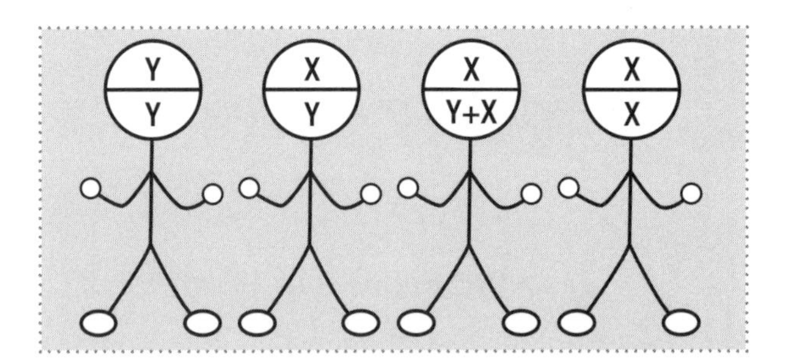

Whatever idea is planted in the subconscious mind will be carried out by the body. When you consciously decide you want something other than what is in the subconscious, there is some *chaos* or disharmony. The body will always take action based on the idea held in the subconscious mind. Even though you want "X," "Y" is still in place in the subconscious mind and will remain the body's ruling thought until it is replaced with a new idea.

Fortunately, the ideas in the subconscious mind *can be* replaced, and that is exactly what we are doing during the reconditioning process by using affirmations, visualizations, meditations, and mental martial arts. Once the new idea is ingrained into the subconscious mind, it takes hold and then causes the body to act in accordance with that new idea. This is the law and, therefore, must work. Our job is to get the idea of what we want implanted into our subconscious mind and then let nature take its course. When we get the new idea implanted, that is when we see amazing results in our lives. This new idea remains there until it is replaced with yet another new idea.

Affirmations—positive statements intended to create new beliefs, actions, or behaviors to accomplish goals—must be repeated on a consistent basis. We are creating new beliefs, and you will soon learn that beliefs are created through repetition. However, there is an exception to the repetition rule. A new belief can be created instantly if a significant emotional event occurs at the moment of thought. For instance, if a dog bites you as you pet him, a belief could materialize that when you pet dogs, they bite.

Emotion Accelerates the Formation of New Beliefs

Emotions increase the speed at which beliefs are created. This is because proteins are released at the synaptic gap. The synaptic gap is the space between the dendrites, which are brain cells that are communicating thoughts among one another. When strong emotions occur, proteins are released at the synaptic gap, which ties the neurons together, binding

The more you fire (think) a thought, the easier it becomes to fire that same thought the next time. Eventually, with enough repetition or emotion, the new thought or belief will become the point of least resistance. After enough repetition, it will be ingrained as a habit.

them and making them stronger and, thus, easier to execute. This allows the thought to be easier to *think* the next time.

Repetition does the same thing over a period of time. Donald Hebb, deemed the father of neuropsychology, said, "Neurons that fire together, wire together." **The more you *fire* (think) a thought, the easier it becomes to *fire* that same thought the next time. Eventually, with enough repetition or emotion, the new thought or belief will become the point of least resistance. After enough repetition, it will be ingrained as a habit.**

When that happens, it will become comparable to an autopilot system. To use the airplane takeoff analogy, once you are airborne (habit is created), you have cleared the tower, and you can ease back on the throttle. Ideally, you would wait until you have reached your cruising altitude, then you can essentially coast. Yes, some effort will be required but a whole lot less than what was needed to take off.

Utilize Nature's Technology

This is where we are striving to get to, where there is no major effort or willpower required. Essentially, the power of the habit or the autopilot program is what reduces the effort required. Ahhhh, technology—you've got to love it!

A habit is an example of one of nature's technologies. Habits make our lives much easier, but they can make them challenging too, depending on whether we did a good job filtering out the bad habits and creating good ones. Habits are so powerful because they are based in the subconscious mind—the powerhouse.

Essentially, the subconscious mind runs your entire life. If you doubt that statement for an instant, then tell me the chemical formula or the group of enzymes needed to digest proteins and how to make them. That's what I thought. Most people don't even know that (consciously) a different enzyme is needed to digest a protein (protease) versus a fat (lipase) or carbohydrate (amylase). Our subconscious mind knows not only which enzyme but also the correct amount to secrete—and when! That is a small fraction of the digestive process and an even smaller part of the entire human system. Subconsciously, we are geniuses!

What about pumping your heart? That is another, entirely different system in your body that is run by your subconscious mind. There are approximately two gallons of blood flowing through miles of veins and arteries, and this is done without one conscious thought. There are many other major systems in our bodies that are run by our subconscious mind. All of these processes can be running while you are talking on the phone, riding your bike, or sleeping, without your spending one moment thinking about it. That is the power of the subconscious mind.

I am quite grateful that I don't have to concern myself with all of these life-maintenance systems. All of them are taken care of automatically. How would you like to put your fitness and exercise program on autopilot? You can do so, and you will if you'll keep reading and applying what we are talking about here.

Let's get back to habits for a more in-depth examination. Every morning, you get dressed for the day. Maybe you shower first and then get dressed. Perhaps your habit is to shower at night. It is rare that you would consciously think about it. Instead, you just do it. That is the manifestation of a habit. At an earlier time, we were *conditioned* or programmed to believe showering and dressing were customary, and, over time, you took action until it became a habit. (Not all prior conditioning is bad.) Now you get dressed automatically.

When we are talking about retraining or reprogramming, we're talking about replacing old habits with new habits. We are setting a new program for our autopilot, and we are employing our subconscious mind to help us.

When you finish getting ready and it is time to go to work, most likely, you take the same route to work without even thinking about it. In fact, you could be on your cell phone talking, and the next thing you know, you're at your destination and don't even remember how you got there. That is your powerful subconscious mind at work. That is an example of a habit.

Habits can be powerful allies, and they can be impressive foes as well. The good news is that, with this book, you have the keys to change your habits, because this book shows you how to reprogram habits. I said that this book shows you how, but I *didn't* say this book will do it for you. You must do the work. This book is only a pile of paper with ink on it. If you are not going to apply the ideas suggested here, then it might as well be a romance novel. It might make you feel good for a while, but it just isn't going to help make anything meaningful happen.

When we are talking about retraining or reprogramming, we're talking about replacing old habits with new habits. We are setting a new program for our autopilot, and we are employing our subconscious mind to help us. We are getting to the source—the cause of our results. Buying a new exercise gadget is not going to improve your fitness level if you only use it for a week or two. In fact, some of the junk being sold won't help you if you used it forever. On the other hand, properly harnessing the power of useful habits can provide you with a very satisfying and perpetual fitness program.

There Is Nothing Wrong with You. It Is Not Your Fault

We are not setting out to bash exercise gadgets here, although it is worth mentioning that some of the gadgets you see on television were not made to help you get in better shape, but only to fatten the wallets of the companies selling them. Profit is good, and I am all for companies making money, but only if they add value to the customers' lives. Every time someone buys a fitness gadget and fails to get fit, it erodes his or her confidence in finding a solution. The exercise industry is estimated to take in $41 billion per year. That is a lot of money, and it should produce products that build people up and yield valuable results.

There are many good exercise tools available, but you can get into the best shape of your life without a gym or expensive exercise equipment. For those getting started or those who know little about exercise, it is wise to seek experts to guide you. Of course, most of us know that if you put an electrified belt around your stomach and turn it on, it will NOT melt away the fat.

As for many of the items advertised repeatedly on TV, surely the svelte, ripped, sexy models they use to promote those gadgets never put those things on until the cameras started rolling. Let's be real. How naïve do they think we are? Obviously, they are hoping to capitalize on the natural desire for a quick and easy fitness remedy—a magic pill. Possibly, the makers of those gadgets attempt to capitalize on our frustration and desperation to get fit. Some people who see their commercials will fall prey to their schemes, but these companies are not really helping those who purchase their products.

In my opinion, numerous advertisers on TV are promoting a sham. They are also perpetuating misinformation that many in our society have been conditioned to expect—something for nothing or results without effort. The real reason those sexy models are in excellent shape and exhibit ripped muscles is that they have *mastered their mindsets*. In other words, they have formed habits to achieve fitness and have stuck with those habits. There is nothing wrong with you, and you can decide to upgrade your mindset also.

> "To enjoy good health, to bring true happiness to one's family, to bring peace to all, one must first discipline and control one's own mind. If a man can control his mind he can find the way to enlightenment, and all wisdom and virtue will naturally come to him."
>
> **—Buddha**

Why Most People Fail with Diet and Exercise Programs

This year, over fifty million Americans will attempt to lose weight. Only 5% will succeed. Ninety-five percent of people *trying* to lose weight will fail. Many will plop down their hard-earned cash on the next diet book, a new gym membership, a diet club, or an exercise gadget, hoping this will finally be the answer to their prayers. Billions of dollars will be spent, and yet only about 5% will succeed. Why? It isn't because of the exercise gadget, the gym membership, the diet club, or books. It *is* because of their mindsets.

Most people are not using their subconscious minds to their advantage. The subconscious mind controls your behavior. If someone has an "I am too lazy to exercise" program running, it doesn't matter how much cash he or she plopped down or how fancy the equipment is. Eventually, he or she will revert back to the old behavior of "I am too lazy to exercise"—unless, of course, this person reprograms that mindset. All the cash the person may have spent was wasted. It may as well have been flushed down the toilet, because now the equipment or gadget sits collecting dust.

How much money have you spent over the years to get and stay fit? Gyms, exercise equipment, and clubs are fine, and many are worth the investment. The key is being ready with the proper mindset. Why do people fail? They lack the proper mindset. How can they change their mindsets? The answer is by reprogramming their minds with the suggestions in this book and, in particular, affirmations, visualizations, mediations, and mental martial arts—by elimination of automatic negative thoughts (ANTs). We will talk more about these concepts later.

The reason the affirmations work is that when you say and repeat positive statements, your mind thinks the thought, which *fires* a neural net (group of cells in the brain). Each time a certain neural net is fired, it becomes stronger. Fire it repeatedly and it continues to get stronger.

A Reprogramming Lesson from a Kid

When I was a child, I used to play in the woods behind my parents' home. It was great fun. Occasionally, I would go out into the middle of the woods and build a fort. "The middle of the woods" meant there were no real trails that led to it. Consequently, I had to create a new trail through the woods, and sometimes that meant right through the "thick of it."

I created a lot of new trails. The first time through, a new trail would be a challenge. I needed an ax, machete, pruners, and a lot of elbow grease. It took quite a bit of effort to create a new trail, and, at the end of each day, I could step back and look at what I had accomplished and be proud of the effort I had put in. I would sometimes think, "Wow, look at what I did today." It was a great reward to see my progress, and, every time, I patted myself on the back. This little act of recognition or celebration helped me want to do more the next day, so the next day, I was out there again.

Sometimes, I would be in the middle of creating a new trail and would ask myself, "What the heck am I doing?" I would think thoughts such as, "This is a huge project; how am I ever going to complete it? Why do I need this new trail?" Keep in mind that this new trailblazing process could take a week or two and, for a kid, that is a long time. It was a big wood!

When I reached the point of being overwhelmed, I would refocus on my objective. I was grateful for what I had already accomplished, and then I looked at what I wanted to accomplish the next day. Thus, I was breaking my goal down into manageable pieces. This approach enabled me to get myself back on track.

Ironically, I didn't learn this technique by reading a book. Something inside of me guided me through this process. I think many times, as kids, we are more in touch with our *higher selves* than we are as adults. However, we can tap into our Source for guidance at any time. During those times of insight, I was tapping in. The Source can guide you, too, when you are open to it. I was able to complete a new trail with the help of the right tools and a good deal of effort. My prize was that, once the trail was blazed, it was a lot easier to get to and from the new fort.

As long as I kept using this new path, it would stay clear. If I neglected it or I didn't use it, it would eventually grow over. It would fill in with weeds and trees and shrubs. In fact, to maintain the trail, all I had to do was use it, which, in this case, was to walk or ride my bike on the trail. If I didn't travel down the trail for a while, the trail would still be there, but it would be grown over to a certain extent. Some maintenance to the trail was required, depending on how much time had passed since I last traveled on it. The longer I went without using it, the more weeds, small trees, and bushes sprouted up, and the less discernible the trail was.

This story is a great metaphor and illustrates what we will go through to create new habits or a new "program." Initially, we are blazing a new trail, and it *does* require effort. **I believe that anything worth having is worth working for.** If it is too easy, you won't appreciate it when you have it. The more you *think* the new thought, say the affirmations, visualize, meditate, and practice mental martial arts by eliminating the ANTs (automatic negative thoughts) the more likely you are to succeed. The clearer that trail is, the easier it is to travel and the more likely you are to continue using that trail, which has become a path of least resistance. Like water, your thoughts will take the path of least resistance. However, you can also guide water to go where you want it, just as you can guide your thoughts to go where you want them to go.

I believe that anything worth having is worth working for.

The good news is that the going gets easier, although it is important to stay focused on your target. You may want to break your target down into manageable chunks while at the same time keeping your eyes on the ultimate prize. It will benefit you to reward yourself and to be grateful for what you have accomplished each and every day. Use this strategy, and you will reach your objective. You will create that new trail to *your new fort,* to your new habit.

TEACHING POINTS

- ☑ Having a picture of your mind enhances understanding.
- ☑ Nature operates automatically; habits are examples of nature's technologies.
- ☑ There is nothing wrong with you, but your mindset may need an overhaul.
- ☑ Most people fail with their diets and exercise programs because they lack the proper mindsets.
- ☑ Initially, reprogramming requires some effort, but the fruits of your labor yield habits that put the majority of effort on autopilot.

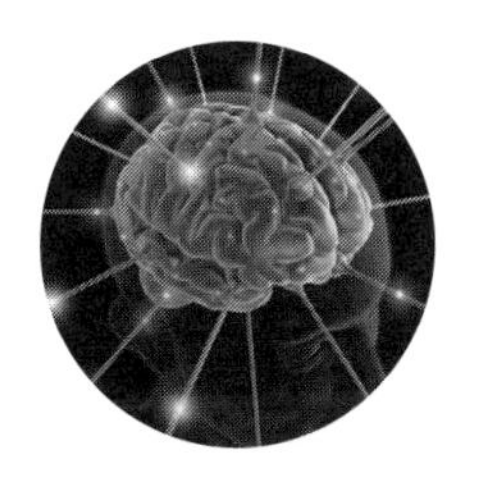

CHAPTER 4

The Great Law and Other Laws of the Universe

"What this power is I cannot say; all I know is that it exists and it becomes available only when a man is in that state of mind in which he knows exactly what he wants and is fully determined not to quit until he finds it."

—Alexander Graham Bell

IF YOU DON'T KNOW THE RULES OF THE GAME, HOW CAN YOU PLAY TO WIN?

Hundreds of years ago, scholars, prophets, and masters revealed numerous interesting forward-thinking ideas, many of which we are now able to prove with science. We understand some of these ideas today as universal laws. When understood and applied, these

Laws of the Universe can make a huge difference in our lives. What would it be like to drive in traffic if you didn't know the traffic laws? It would be chaotic. Drivers who know the laws but don't adhere to them also create chaotic situations. The same is true in life. If you don't know the Universal Laws or you know them and don't adhere to them, you may create a less-than-desirable result.

If you are playing a game with friends and you don't know the rules of the game, the likelihood of your winning is nil. After a while, you may become irritated and frustrated and wonder why you are playing this game in the first place. Most likely, you will give up and quit. Playing a game without knowing the rules is like baking cookies without a recipe. You are guessing. After many attempts and several tweaks, you might make something edible and maybe even tasty, but, would it not be so much quicker and easier if you used a recipe or followed the advice of a wise mentor? Once you know the recipe, you can make cookies (or whatever the recipe is for) on your own and they have a greater chance of tasting good. The same is true with knowing and applying the Laws of the Universe. How can you play the game of life without knowing the rules of the universe? You can, but it will not be as much fun and you wouldn't really be playing full-on.

When I first learned of these laws, nothing major happened. However, as they began to sink in to my consciousness, a new understanding began to develop, which enabled me to reach new heights. We will begin with the Great Law.

The Great Law Is "Energy Is"

Albert Einstein disclosed this law many years ago when he revealed the world's most famous formula, $E = MC^2$. My interpretation of the formula is mass is energy. We are all energy. Everything is energy. If we are energy, and everything else is energy, then *all is energy*. From a star to a car, everything is made of energy. Therefore, you can infer that we all originate from energy or the same Source and that we are all connected and are all one.

Not too far from where I live, two men who had never made a movie before decided to make a documentary based on the premise that we are all one. In fact, the title of the movie is *One*. I encourage you to get a copy of that movie and watch it.

If you ask a scientist, he or she will tell you that everything is made of energy. Energy always was, is now, and always will be. It can never be created or destroyed. It only changes form. Scientists will also tell you that energy constantly changes form.

If you ask a religious leader, he or she will tell you that God always was, is now, and always will be. God can never be created or destroyed. When you take a closer look, you will realize these people are talking about the same thing. The only difference is the name. When you grasp the idea that God and Energy *are* the same thing, you will be on the right track.

Why is this concept important to understand? We are made of energy. We are a part of God. The Bible says, "So God created man in his own image…." Why does this concept matter? With it, we can stop beating ourselves down and start living our lives abundantly, as we were intended to do. *We* can take control of *our* thoughts and direct and focus them on what *we* choose to create in *our* lives. We are energy!

The Law of Perpetual Transmutation of Energy

The Law of Perpetual Transmutation of Energy suggests that energy is always changing form, everything is either growing or dying, nothing stays the same, and change is constant. From the Great Law, we know that everything is energy, so, our thought of having our ideal life and ideal body is either growing (moving toward us) or dying (moving away from us).

We need to focus on the thoughts of our ideal body (or life) to understand the Law of Perpetual Transmutation, to incorporate the Law of Cause and Effect (every cause has an effect and every effect has a cause), and take action, which is the cause of the effect that we are seeking. If we neglect these things, our concept of our ideal body or ideal life will be in a declining state or dying. When we keep focused and realize that there is a gestation period and that for every cause—thought, feeling, and action—there is an effect, and when we think the thoughts of our ideal body, sense the feelings, and take the actions, our ideal body is arising or thriving.

The Law of Relativity

The Law of Relativity suggests that nothing is good or bad or big or small until you relate it to something else. Comparably, in *your* present state, nothing is either good or bad until *you* relate it to something else. Depending on what you relate it to determines in what condition you decide it is. If you are five feet tall and weigh 175 pounds and someone of the same sex and about the same age and height weighs 225 pounds, you may think you are in decent shape when you *relate* your body to his or hers.

However, if you compare yourself to someone who weighs 145 pounds, you might not hold such an enthusiastic view of yourself. It is all relative. Going forward, I encourage you to avoid comparing yourself to others—only to your ideal self. This is *not* a competition with others. This *is* an opportunity to grow and evolve in relation to your *past* self. What does your ideal self look like and what does it weigh? When you do compare your present self to your ideal self, do not beat yourself up. Your current self is based on old thinking, and we are changing that with the information being shared here and the application of that knowledge.

The Law of Attraction (or Vibration)

The Law of Attraction (or Vibration) suggests everything vibrates and nothing rests. Everything has its own vibration or frequency, and like attracts like. You can incorporate this law by focusing on exactly what you *want*. If you desire to lose forty pounds, do not focus on losing forty pounds. Instead, focus on the weight you will be after you shed the forty pounds. **This is the frequency at which you want to vibrate.**

In my case, my weight rose to almost 220 pounds, and I decided on my ideal weight of 190 pounds. I did **NOT** think at all about losing 30 pounds. Instead, my focus was on weighing 190 pounds. I began to "vibrate" at 190 pounds, and then, after a relatively short period of time, I was not only vibrating at 190, I was 190! **Keep your focus on what you want and you will begin to vibrate at that frequency. Once you vibrate at the new level, you become that new level.** This applies to everything you are striving to accomplish.

An AM/FM radio is a good example of the Law of Attraction. If there is a particular station you like to listen to, you dial in to that frequency. If you choose to listen to 94.7 FM, you wouldn't tune in to 1600 AM. You decide on a station (goal), and you tune in to it. Each radio station is broadcasting at a certain frequency. To pick up that frequency, you must tune in to it. **The way you consciously use The Law of Attraction (LOA) is by tuning in to the frequency of your objective or goal.**

If you desire to lose 40 pounds, do not focus on losing 40 pounds. Instead, focus on the weight you will be after you shed the 40 pounds.

The way you consciously use The Law of Attraction (LOA) is by tuning in to the frequency of your objective or goal.

The Law of Polarity

The Law of Polarity indicates that everything has an opposite. If there is a front, there must be a back. If there is a top, there must be a bottom. If you have a problem, there **MUST** be a solution. If a part of you doesn't want to exercise today, a part of you *does* want to exercise today. Some people believe that for every positron in the universe there is an electron. How can this benefit us? Understanding this concept can help us keep moving toward our goals, even when "stuff" happens, because we know there must be a positive in the situation somewhere. It can assist us by reminding us to focus on the good because the bad is there too. When we focus on the good, we begin to vibrate at that frequency, and then we attract more "good."

The Law of Rhythm

The Law of Rhythm implies that everything operates in a rhythm. Day follows night, spring follows winter, fall follows summer, the tides ebb, and the tides flow in. Assuming that everything operates in a rhythm, how can we use this principle to our benefit? When we realize that there are *seasons*, we understand that *things may not always go our way*. This knowledge can help ease our frustrations, so that we can relax and enjoy the journey of life, knowing there is a rhythm to all of existence. By accepting that sometimes life ebbs and sometimes it flows, we are also reminded that there is a gestation period for our goals.

The Law of Cause and Effect

The Law of Cause and Effect suggests that every cause has an effect and every effect has a cause. Science confirms this ancient philosophical idea with Newton's third law of motion: *for every action there is an equal and opposite reaction.*

Every thought you think has an effect. Every feeling you sense and every action you take has an effect. If you don't like the effects (results) you are presently enjoying (or not enjoying), then you need to change your thoughts, feelings, and/or actions. Even though you don't see the effects immediately, they *are* happening and will appear in their due time. When you know the effect you want to achieve, the next step is to figure out what causes need to be implemented. Next, implement that/those cause/causes, and the effects (results) materialize. Concentrate your efforts on the cause, and the effect will take care of itself.

The Law of Gender

The Law of Gender (creation or gestation) suggests every seed (physical, mental, and spiritual) has a gestation or incubation period. Thoughts and ideas are seeds too. Every idea you have or goal you set has a gestation period. When you are striving so diligently toward your objective and it seems slow to materialize, you may want to consider the Law of Gender. When you realize that "things" take time to happen, you can curtail some, if not all, of your frustration. You can continue with your faith and remain steadfast in your duties to accomplish whatever you are striving for.

Do not fret when the time runs out. Be patient! Your objective will happen. It may only mean that we need to keep moving forward with conviction and determination. It could mean we need to make some adjustments. God's delays are not God's denials.

When we look at nature, nothing really **happens** in an instant. It is a process. Sure lightning strikes, but it takes time for all the clouds to gather. Somewhere in the cycle, water evaporates into the sky and water molecules gather to form clouds. At first, the clouds are small; then they become bigger. Eventually, *when conditions are right*, they form rain clouds. If conditions remain ideal, they form storm clouds, and, finally, when those conditions are right, and only when those conditions are right, lightning strikes.

We all want "lightning" to strike, and most of us want it now. My friend, **as soon as you realize this is a process, life will be a lot easier for you.** You can decide now that you want "lightning" to strike, which for you could mean six-pack abs, to be thin, a certain pant size, or to be at a certain weight. The important thing is to decide what you want. It is also important to realize that it does take time.

We know about how long it takes for many plants to grow. However, for the seed of your desire, we don't really know exactly how long it will take. It depends on many variables in your life. Just as the growth of the seed is affected by the soil, sun, temperature, and other variables, so too are the "seeds" of desire, and those variables influence the gestation period.

Recently, my family and I planted a small garden beside our home. On the back of a seed packet, it states the approximate gestation period for that type of seed. For carrots, the gestation period is seventy to ninety days. Wouldn't it be nice to know how long it will take to "grow" our ideas or desires? Because we don't yet possess that information, we need to make our best guess when setting the time lines on our goals. Develop a time frame for your goals based on the information you possess and then work toward that time line. If the target date has come and gone and the goal is not achieved, set a new date and continue moving toward it.

Throughout this book we will continue to discuss ideas that tie in to these laws. Keep a sharp eye out for these laws and what they mean for your journey to success. When you accept these laws, you are more likely to stay on track and persevere, because you understand that real scientific rules are at work. Ultimately, you will come to recognize that these laws need to be adhered to in order to achieve your objectives.

Knowing these laws is like knowing the rules to a game. If you don't know the rules, your chance for victory is limited, at best. If you know them, you have a greater chance to win. In the game of life, not only will your odds increase, but, when you *apply* the laws, you win. Read, study, and apply these laws in your life, and watch what positive things happen.

"The most impactful exercise you can do is to lift your thoughts."

—Don Staley

TEACHING POINTS

- ☑ Knowing the rules enhances success.
- ☑ Everything is energy.
- ☑ Energy is always changing forms.
- ☑ Nothing is either good or bad or big or small until you relate it to something else. Then, only deciding makes it so.
- ☑ Everything vibrates, and like vibrations attract like vibrations.
- ☑ There are always two sides to every coin.
- ☑ Everything operates in a rhythm.
- ☑ Every cause has an effect.
- ☑ Every seed (mental or physical) has an incubation period.

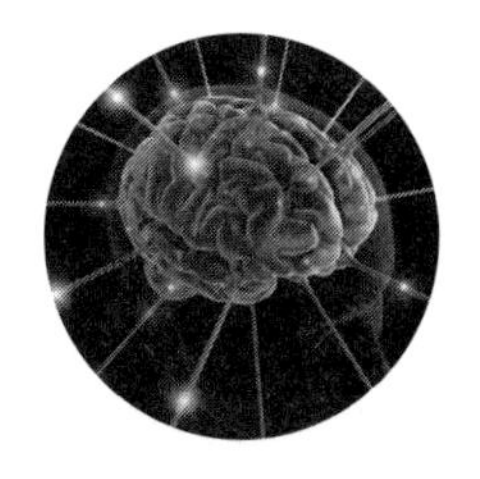

CHAPTER 5

Responsibility

"If it is to be, it's up to me."

—Dennis Waitley

If It Is to Be, It Is Up to Me

Your success is *your* responsibility and no one else's! I remember hearing this statement many years ago. However, it took me a while before it finally sunk in. I did not want to take responsibility for certain things, such as my thoughts. Believe it or not, we are responsible for the thoughts we hold in our minds. Notice I didn't say "the thoughts that enter the mind." I said "the thoughts *held in* the mind." Holding a thought is to keep thinking a thought.

There were times when I didn't think I was responsible for my thoughts. I asked myself, "How can I control my thoughts?" Then, I thought, "I don't possess the power." (That thought is an automatic negative thought, an ANT.) In reality, I *did* have the power. All I needed was to realize I did possess the power and develop that ability. It is a skill, and, like so many things, this skill improves with practice.

Blame Weakens You

Assume that you know your true desire. If you are willing to take personal responsibility and *stop blaming* others or circumstances, then we're on the way to making your desire a reality. Elimination of blame is critical to your success. Eliminating blame may be a challenge, depending on how much you have relied on it as a crutch. The more you leaned on blame in the past, the more challenging it will be to rid yourself of it.

When you blame, you give up your power.

We have all heard people say that they don't have enough time to exercise. Actually, we all have the same amount of time—twenty-four hours in a day. "Not enough time" is an excuse. **Be careful not to rationalize your way out of success.** Remember, "rationalize" can be broken down into two words*: rational lies*. Rationalizing and making up stories, even if they seem true, are excuses and thus are lacking in personal responsibilities.

Perhaps what they were really saying is that they haven't yet learned how to manage their day in respect to time. If you are guilty of blaming (I was too), then I challenge you to avoid blaming the clock or anything else. The good news is that after you learn about reconditioning your mind, you will have a great advantage to assist you in moving forward.

This world is filled with many possibilities. Is your desire of __________ possible? Is your dream of _________ possible? I say it is. If you will adhere to the steps in the following chapters, you will attain your desire. No more blaming your genes. **When you blame, you give up your power.** Why would you ever choose to give up your power? No more saying, "I'm big-boned." Yes, that may be true, but it doesn't mean you should be fat, too. There is a difference between possessing a larger structure or frame and being fat. As you shed the excuses, you shed the excess pounds.

When I finally decided to get fit once and for all, I took responsibility. I realized that in my life "things happen," and I would need to be flexible and go with the flow. However, I still needed to perform what needed to get done. When I began, one of my biggest realizations was the **process of reprogramming**. In this process, the most efficient way to create a new habit is to diligently perform the task you want to develop every day for a minimum of thirty days. Of course, I encountered obstacles along the way.

I believe that obstacles are one way the universe tests whether we are serious. On occasion, it would have been easy to say, "My child is sick. How can anyone expect me to exercise today?" There were a handful of days when I could have said that. There were days when I could have said, "It's too late to exercise and I'm too tired." I remember several of those days, and it would have been easy to blame a multitude of things. However, ultimately, I took responsibility. Now, I enjoy the benefits.

It doesn't matter what happens during the day. If my intention is to exercise daily and it is 11 p.m. without my having exercised, it is not the fault of the day. It is my fault. When I first began my new exercise regimen, there were many nights when things were busy, hectic, or frantic. When 11 p.m. rolled around and I still hadn't exercised, it would have been very easy to toss in the towel. Such moments are the critical turning points. Fortunately, I decided to take responsibility. I took action and did what needed to be done.

I used, and still do, the same tools, techniques, and strategies that you will learn here to overcome such mental challenges. I accepted responsibility. I took action and completed my exercise. Eventually, exercising every day became a habit, and now daily exercise is automatic for me. It rarely requires much effort to "do it." **When you take responsibility for your desires, you can develop powerful habits** such as these also.

Your Ticket to Paradise

A really exciting aspect of taking responsibility for your actions is the freedom you feel. You will feel empowered as well. In the 1995 movie *Braveheart,* Mel Gibson played the character William Wallace, who desired freedom for Scotland. In the story, Wallace encountered many obstacles. He didn't blame the government, his comrades, or even the situation. He simply assumed responsibility, and he took the actions he needed to take to advance toward his goal. One of my favorite quotations from that movie is, "Every man dies, but not every man really lives." Also, my other favorite line, which is only a word, is fitting here, because taking responsibility will ultimately gain your freedom. Toward the end of the movie, Wallace is being tortured to get him to confess. Regardless of the pain and suffering, he holds true to his cause and yells out, "FREEDOM!"

When you take responsibility for your desires, you can develop powerful habits.

Even though Wallace's country wasn't technically free, he lived his life as if he were free—and so he was. Admittedly, this movie contains some violent scenes, but if you look deeper, you'll see it is more about freedom and responsibility than violence.

We are talking now about **personal freedom from our old conditioning**. It comes down to your making a decision. Only you can decide. Then and only then will you take the necessary actions to accomplish your goals. I decided I was going to write this book, and, of course, you decided you were going to read it. Unless I understood this concept of responsibility, I would not have awakened early every day for a year—sometimes as early as 5 a.m.—to write. **Accomplishment starts with a desire and then taking responsibility.** Will you take responsibility for your success by shouting the word "freedom" for your old conditioning to hear?

You need to create a clear vision, in great detail, of exactly what it is you desire.

What is it you truly want? Do you know what it is? What does your ideal body look like? How does it feel to live in your ideal body? Are you willing to take personal responsibility to become aware of and achieve your ideal body? If so, you are ready to move to the next step of this process. You need to **create a clear vision, in great detail, of exactly what it is you desire.**

The Buck Stops Here!

The buck stops here! It stops with *you*. Taking personal responsibility is number one. Until you take personal responsibility for your results, you will not take the actions required, because you don't believe **your success ultimately depends on you. It DOES!** Only by doing what must be done will you get what you want! Are you willing to take personal responsibility for your thoughts, feelings, and actions?

TEACHING POINTS

- ☑ If it is to be, it is up to YOU.
- ☑ Blaming is giving your power away.
- ☑ Taking personal responsibility is your ticket to freedom.
- ☑ The buck stops here, with you.

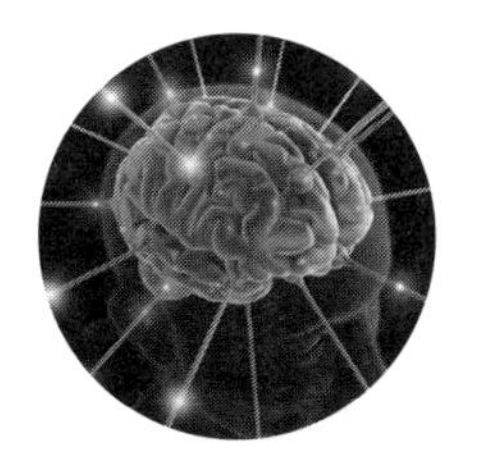

CHAPTER 6

DESIRE

"Follow your bliss."

—Joseph Campbell

What Do You Want?

DESIRE. What is your desire? What do you really want? **Focus *not* on what you *think* you can achieve or what you have been *conditioned to believe* you can achieve but rather what you really, truly want.** Throughout this book, I invite you to revisit an old skill. Possibly, it is a dormant skill you have neglected for a long time—using your imagination. The pretending we did as kids was and is a good thing. We are going to revive that skill, so let's get started. Imagine, if you will, encountering a magical genie who can grant you any wish. Besides wishing for more wishes, what would you really, truly yearn for? If you could do, be, or have anything, what would it be? Remember, it is *not* what you think you can have but what you *truly want.*

What would you alter about your body in regard to health, nutrition, and fitness? How much energy and vitality do you want? Do you wish to glow with confidence?

These questions may require some soul-searching, and if that is the only thing you take away from this piece of work, it will be many times more valuable than your time and effort exerted plus the cost (investment) of the book. Let's look at one way to examine what your ultimate desire is for your well-being. Years ago I was searching for what I wanted to do with my life. The old saying "I know deep down" wasn't really that deep down for me, because it kept popping up at me.

Old Negative Programming or Conditioning Held You Back

The challenge was that my programming at the time had me conditioned to believe I could not do what I thought I wanted. Deep down, I realized that I wanted to speak to groups and help as many people as possible. The desire I kept ignoring was to speak professionally as a coach to people's success. At the time, I thought, "How can I coach people to success if I haven't yet succeeded?" It was a good question. My goal was to empower people, but I didn't feel empowered. I kept pushing my desire down every time it popped up, and I did this for years. Do you know anyone like that?

Because of my lack of positive conditioning, I did not believe I was worthy to be so bold as to tell other people how to achieve. At the same time, I was looking for the next best option for my fallback career until someday I would be able to pursue my true desire. I knew that I wanted to be self-employed and work from home. Other than that, I wasn't exactly sure what my fallback position should be.

Knowing Your Aversions Can Lead to Your Desires

At that time, I was taking a three-day course about starting a business. When I wrote down all the things I did *not* want to do, this action illuminated all the things I did want. I was employing the Law of Polarity, which suggests everything has an opposite. Seeing the exact opposites of what I didn't want was a good start toward realizing what I did want. I made my list of *don't wants* and then looked for the polar opposites. Amazingly, I found what I did want to do.

Making that list helped me tremendously in determining my next career. Making a similar list for yourself can aid you in discovering what it is you do want. For years prior, I went from one career to the next, because I pushed down what I really wanted, due to my conditioning. Have you ever let this happen in your life?

Eventually, I was led to many answers to questions I had been asking myself for over twenty years. I had discovered the Law of Attraction!

Make a list of what you do not want and then determine the exact opposites of each item on that list. Doing this exercise will help determine what you do want. By finding the polar opposites of the items on your do-not-want list, you are narrowing down your target. See the list below as an example. Now make your own list.

I do NOT want to be...	Polar opposite	I DO want to be... (or something similar)
heavy*	→	at my ideal weight of "y" pounds
fat	→	lean
tired	→	energetic
stressed	→	calm, peaceful
lazy	→	industrious, productive
sick	→	healthy

**The polar opposite of "heavy" is light or thin, so, in all cases, it won't be exactly the polar opposite, but it leads you toward what you do want.*

For many people, determining what they do NOT want is a great place to start fleshing out their desires. Once you have isolated your "don't wants," avoid thinking of them and begin to focus on what you *do* want. What you focus on will grow or expand. After this exercise, continue to focus only on what you *do* want. Limiting, monitoring, and choosing your thoughts may be a challenge, and we'll learn more about how to do exactly that when we talk about ANTs (automatic negative thoughts).

Determining what you *do* want and spotlighting your passion may take some time. You can read more about finding your passion in the book I coauthored entitled *The Power of Mentorship: Finding Your Passion,* published by Real Life Teaching/Publishing (2008). It is available through my website, www.DonStaley.com. Many teachers, coaches, mentors, and authors worked together on that project to present many different perspectives. In that book are more ideas on how to find your passion.

Once you know what you want, go for it! When setting goals, make sure you're reaching and stretching. Your present conditioning may be hindering your true heart's desire from happening. Be cognizant of this possibility and reach for the stars.

Isn't it time for you to have what you really want from life? You deserve real fulfillment and happiness. Everyone does! It is my belief that we are all capable of determining what will make us happy, even though it may require some soul-searching. Your passions are inside you. When you let them out, you will enjoy much more of life. Our Higher Self sends us messages, but, most likely, they are being pushed down by our conditioning, which took place throughout every moment of our lives.

Negative influences have told us more than ten thousand times "No, you can't" or something comparable. Some estimates are that by the time we are teenagers, we hear "NO!" fifty thousand times. Compare this with the estimate that we hear "YES!" only five to ten thousand times. Hearing too many negatives can create doubt in our minds and stymies our true selves.

Our Higher Self seeks to express itself through the larger goal, while our conditioned self tries to protect itself by suppressing the higher desire. Thus, we go on with our lives with smaller, more acceptable and achievable wishes or goals. Maybe, because we are suppressing, we don't gain a real sense of what our real passion is, even though it attempts to reveal itself by popping up occasionally.

When you release those negative thoughts and allow your Higher Self to come forth, you allow the answers to all of your questions to flow to you. When you obtain these solutions, you finally become clear on what you are to do. By acquiring clarity on exactly what you are going to trade your life for, it becomes less like work and more like fun. Yes, there will be work to do, but it is a different kind of labor. This is an exertion you are inspired to complete. The difference is like night and day. You see, your true self has something of great value to offer, and it is time that you began to deliver it. The world is waiting for YOU to deliver. The world is longing for your dream to be fulfilled, and when you succeed, we all benefit.

For a moment, consider your desire to be fit and healthy. Do you think if you are out of shape, fat, and lazy that you are serving the world? Technically, you are, but think on a larger scale. Is that how you want to serve? Seek to understand the big picture. Maybe serving the world doesn't concern you. In that case, does being out of shape really serve *you*? When you are in excellent physical shape, you perform better in all areas of your life. You will burn through stress like a hot knife through butter and you will be more energetic and more inspired and will perform better in whatever you do. Would you like to experience more and better sex? You WILL have better sex! Would that benefit alone be worth getting yourself into great shape?

The point is, you really know what it is you want to do. Chances are good that you, like many others, have been pushing your true desire down whenever it attempts to reveal itself. My suggestion is to let your passion come out, no matter how big it is. If you were not able to bring it to reality, you would not have received the message that your passion exists. You can do it, and I'm going to show you how.

"Even the least among you can do everything I have done, and even greater things."

— Jesus

Wishes Are Weak; Desires Are Powerful

What ***is*** it you truly ***want***? Your idea or vision must not be merely a wish. If it is just a wish, more than likely, you will not get it. It needs to be a *strong desire,* and I'll tell you why. There will be obstacles, and if your vision isn't something you truly DESIRE, you will abandon the weak vision at the first major obstacle you encounter. The reason it needs to be a *strong desire* is that you will need the emotional charge of your desire to *help* pull you through those challenging times. **Emotions can energize you during tough times.** If it is a wish, most likely there will be little emotion, and, if you lack the necessary emotion, good luck! Make it a desire, not a wish!

"If wishes were horses, beggars would ride" is a part of an old English nursery rhyme, which is often used to suggest that wishing is useless; better results will be achieved through action, and actions starts with a burning desire. Human nature suggests that we won't act on a wish, but a desire inspires us.

In fact, unless *your* desire to achieve your ideal body or ideal life is strong enough to hold your thoughts on this goal, just as a missile locks onto its target, it will hardly be worthwhile for you to carry out the instructions presented in the following chapters. You see, **the ideas and strategies I am presenting here are for those people who have a strong desire to achieve their ideal bodies and are willing to overcome mental laziness and inaction.**

What is it you really want to choose for your life? What is it you desire for your health and fitness? I assume that you want to be fit and healthy and that you want to be energetic. When you climb a flight of stairs, you don't want to pant like a greyhound that just finished a race.

There are about a dozen ideas I have found that have significantly helped me create empowering habits and my ideal body. These ideas helped because of my strong desire to reach my goal.

TEACHING POINTS

- ☑ What you truly want may be different from what you believe you can have.
- ☑ Prior negative conditioning (programming) has stymied the achievement of your true desire.
- ☑ Finding your aversions or dislikes is a way to discover what you do like or desire.
- ☑ Wishes are weak; desires are powerful.
- ☑ Desires inspire.

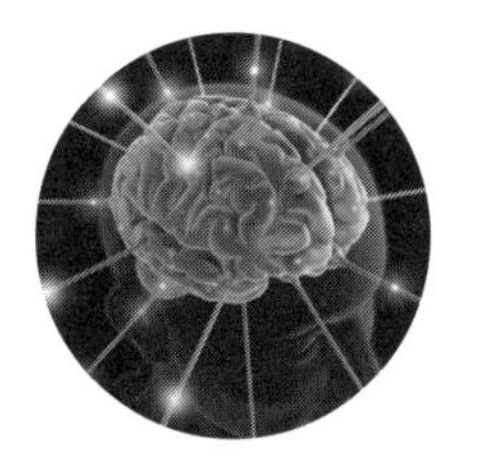

CHAPTER 7

Clear Vision

> "Imagination gives you the picture. Vision gives you the impulse to make the picture your own."
>
> —Robert Collier

Creating a clear vision of exactly what you want or desire can get you excited about your goal. This chapter takes the previous chapter on desire to the next level by going deeper. When you begin writing the details, you build a network of cells in your brain. This is a process that leads to the fulfillment of your dream.

Clear Vision Locks In a Target

To focus precisely on my intended desire, I wrote down clarifying details, which helped me produce a clear vision. I created a crystal-clear target. If you don't have a target, how can you reach it? At the time I began the reconditioning process, I weighed about 216 pounds. I had acquired a flabby, 35-inch waist, and I wasn't fit by any standards. At six feet, two inches tall, those numbers may not seem too terribly bad. However, they were a fatty 216 pounds on my thin body frame. My original goal was to weigh 195 pounds. After some progress and more clarity, I ultimately decided on 190 pounds. My intention was to have a 32-inch waist, a size I hadn't seen in a long while. I also envisioned a lean and ripped "six pack" abdomen. To top this list, I intended to be healthy and energetic. I wanted all of these details to represent the new me.

Staying fit is a lifetime program.

Clear Vision Inspires

With these detailed characteristics, I now had a clear vision of my ideal body. I had a destination or target. One critical point is that I did not want to revert back to a fat me once I got to my target self. Instead, my objective was to obtain that desired level of fitness, make an evaluation, do some tweaking, and then continue to an even greater fitness level. Getting and, more importantly, staying fit is not a ninety-day program. **Staying fit is a lifetime program.** My desire for you and me is a long and healthy lifetime. I desire that you hit your target as quickly as it is healthy for you to do so, because the sooner you do so, the more you can enjoy life to its fullest. What is most important is for you to continue moving in the right direction. At the very least, you need to maintain your target.

Asking Yourself Exploratory Questions Fleshes Out the Details

Can you list several details of your desire? What *specifically* would you like to experience in your life? What does your ideal body look like? Following are a few questions to ask yourself to create the clarity required for your mental picture:

1. What is your ideal weight?
2. What is your ideal waist size?
3. What is your ideal dress or pant size?
4. What is your ideal body-fat content?
5. What is your ideal blood pressure?
6. What is your ideal resting heart rate?
7. How do you feel being in your ideal health?

The Power of Focus

When we get our desires crystal clear, we are harnessing and focusing energy into a smaller area, similar to what a magnifying glass or a laser does.

Many of us played with a magnifying glass when we were children and harnessed the sun's rays to a specific point. Some of us may have ignited paper or caused dead grass to burn with this focused energy. Sunlight is a very powerful energy source as it is, and when you focus its energy, its power intensifies.

On the other hand, if you keep moving the lens around, it won't have a clear target and, thus, will lack focus. Consequently, that lens will not be able to ignite anything. When you get clear on what you want to ignite and you place the focus of the lens on that specific item, it will ignite before too long. This is something you can see almost immediately.

If you compare different light sources, such as incandescent bulbs to lasers, you will notice that the more focused laser beam can project light a much greater distance. The reason is that lasers can project a condensed beam of light in a concentrated and focused pattern because the light waves are synchronized and are emitted with the same wavelength. In other words, there are no conflicting waves messing with the intended wave. Have you ever heard someone say "We are on the same wavelength"? That means harmony has been reached between a number of people.

A Clear Vision Helps Harmonize Your Thoughts

Those people in harmony are able to work more effectively together toward their combined goal because they are on the same wavelength. This means there is no depletion of energy due to multiple, competing, or contradicting agendas, magnification of power, or dilution of energy. These are the same benefits you can use when you develop a crystal clear vision. Become a laser. Gather your clarity. Some lasers are quite powerful. You are also powerful and even more potent when you create a clear vision and make a decision to acquire and own it.

How I Developed a Clear Vision and How You Can Too!

I found a photo of a very fit-looking guy in a fitness magazine, and I cut it out. You can find a good image of your ideal body in magazines or on the Internet. I then superimposed my face over his face. Even though I am not a professional graphic artist, I was able to produce a pretty realistic image of me with my ideal body. I am sure that a professional could have produced a much better image, but it looked pretty convincing without any added expense, and I felt good when I looked at it. Wow! Did I look great!

Find a Picture of Your Ideal Body

I made copies and put these pictures everywhere I could see them. After a week or two, I realized this wasn't my current ideal body. It was the ideal body I wanted back in college. Again, I searched until I found a fit-looking model who wasn't huge and who was in good shape. Then, I replaced all my former modified ideal-body photos. Having placed my face on this new guy's body, I soon realized that I had found my ideal body, and I felt much better, because this new target resonated with me. The first image was what I wanted as a kid and was a good place to start. I had to start somewhere, and my first attempt actually led me to more clarity and the next ideal body image. You will find your ideal image as well, but **you have to start by taking action**. Find an image of *your* ideal body, which is at least in the direction of what you desire and, hopefully, is a bit of a stretch.

Once I realized my *true* desire, I changed the picture to a more "ideal me" picture. What does your "ideal body" look like? Find your ideal body image and superimpose your face on it. Be sure this image is the ideal body you truly want, and post it everywhere that you will see it. Take note that I did not switch pictures because I feared being unable to achieve it. I did believe, but as I developed more clarity, I realized that this "ideal body" wasn't the body I wanted. Then, I modified my ideal image to resonate with my current desire.

Once you have a vision of what you desire, it is normal to tweak it as you progress until you have a *clear* vision. If you already know your desire, this could happen quickly. If you are still in a discovery mode, it could take a bit longer. When you do find your ideal image, make a decision to obtain it. In the next chapter, you will learn more about making that decision.

TEACHING POINTS

- ☑ A clear vision locks in a target.
- ☑ A clear vision inspires action.
- ☑ A clear vision creates and strengthens a neural network of brain cells.
- ☑ Asking yourself exploratory questions fleshes out the details.
- ☑ Find an image of your ideal body.

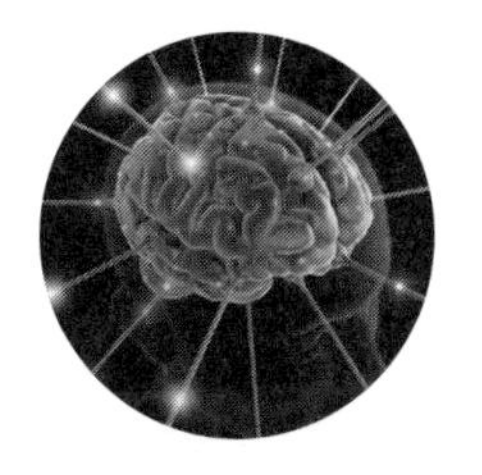

CHAPTER 8

Decision

"When you have to make a choice and don't make it, that is in itself a choice."

—William James

A very powerful step in the process of achieving your objective is making a decision. And, if developing yourself to meet your ideal body image is your objective, then it is time to make a few decisions. **First, decide what your ideal body looks like (create a clear vision); then decide to do WHATEVER it takes to achieve it.** The origin of the word "decide" is to cut off all other possibilities.

To me, there are no other options. "Failure is not an option" is a famous quotation from the movie *Apollo 13*. In the movie, the people responsible at NASA desired to bring the crew home safely, they decided to find a solution, and they did. To decide on your ideal body or ideal life, it means **you will NOT accept anything other than "living" your ideal body.**

Making a Decision Sets Unseen Forces in Motion

When I finally decided to get fit for the rest of my life, in essence, it was as though I had turned on a light switch, which started a series of events to transpire. All of these occurrences then led me to my success. Interesting events started happening. It was as though the universe said, "Finally, Don, you mean it. Here you go. Here are the things you need to make this happen."

Information, people, books, and inspiration showed up in my life, and these were critical elements in helping me achieve my objective. In one case, I received an email, which led me to invest in an eBook, which was loaded with a critical exercise and very useful nutritional information. Upon reading this new information, I quickly corrected some erroneous eating habits and soon shed several stubborn pounds. This "answer," or strategy, didn't present itself until I made the *decision,* and it was very powerful.

Instead of simply wanting to look good for summertime on the beach, I decided to become fit for life, because, if I was going to make a contribution in the way I believed I was capable of, I had to be energetic, confident, powerful, and in great physical (as well as mental and spiritual) shape. I had to be physically fit.

My reason was and is big. Can you list ten reasons you should make a decision to have your ideal body?

When the WHY Is Big Enough, the Decision Is Easy

One day, after lunch with my family, my son asked if he could have a cookie. On this particular occasion, I instantly blurted out, "If you eat some spinach, you can have a cookie." Because he wasn't a big fan of spinach, I figured he would drop the idea. Sometimes kids will surprise you when you least expect it. When I made the offer, he instantly agreed with, "OK."

I brought out some spinach and put it in a bowl. Then, I grabbed a cookie, poured some milk, and put them in front of him as his reward. Now, I don't normally require him to eat a spinach salad before he eats a cookie, but this time, for whatever reason, I did. He decided it was worth eating a small bowl of spinach to earn the cookie. Eat it he did, and I was truly impressed by the power of a four-year-old's *decision* to attain a cookie.

"When the WHY is big enough, making a decision is easy and powerful."

—Don Staley

Making a Decision Is Powerful

A real decision eliminates all other options. **When no other option is present, you possess a focus, which brings you tremendous power. This power helps you take the actions you need to reach your objectives.**

The power of decision-making is amazing. You might know someone who has been "trying" to quit smoking cigarettes for years but "couldn't" do it. He or she may have tried all kinds of methods—gum, the patch, hypnosis—all to no avail. Then, one day, this person may have gotten fed up, made a decision, and thrown away the cigarettes for good.

Benefits Begin Instantly with Certain Decisions

My dad quit smoking instantly when I was a kid. Fortunately, he didn't have to die to do it. All smokers will quit eventually. It is the method that is yet to be determined. He smoked like a chimney—at least a pack a day.

Then, one day, he got infuriated at the negative repercussions of smoking cigarettes, and he threw them away. He never smoked a cigarette again. In fact, he then complained about smokers and public places filled with cigarette smoke. He avoided such places, and I didn't blame him. I avoid those places too. He made the decision, and then he quit.

Author's note: I am looking forward to the day when we, as a society, finally make a decision to ban smoking in all public places. I am not one for more laws, but I am for others' and my right to breathe clean air. Smoke doesn't stay in the smoking sections. Fortunately, some progressive states have already made public places safer and cleaner with laws that prohibit smoking inside public buildings. I would prefer that smokers quit on their own, so no additional laws would be necessary to keep the air clean. We would all be healthier.

Until the behavioral concepts, such as the ideas presented here of how to change the programming of the subconscious, reach the masses—so that they can "reset" their autopilots—most smokers will continue to let their conditioning run their autopilots. I prefer to breathe clean air, not second-hand smoke from someone who hasn't yet made the decision to breathe only clean air. If you know of someone who still smokes, please give him or her a copy of this book and encourage him or her to read it. You may be saving that person's life and, at the same time, helping us all.

My friend Brian and I were mountain biking years ago. We pedaled up some decent hills with some low-to-medium technical trails. We were going up one hill, and Brian was keeping pace with me. I said, "Brian, I am impressed. Even though you smoke, you are still keeping up with me." I didn't mean anything by that comment, except that usually people who smoke have a lesser lung capacity. It struck a chord with him. Happily, I found out about a month or so later that Brain smoked his last cigarette that night. He threw them away for good and became a nonsmoker. Maybe what

I said made him think about his health. It was his decision to quit that enabled him to throw his cigarettes away for good.

A friend of mine says, "People don't smoke, they suck. The cigarette smokes, but the person sucks." It's a funny way to put it, and, technically, he is correct. Perhaps, if you or someone you know is still sucking smoky air, this way of looking at things could help you or your friend make a healthier decision. Of course, the principle is transferable, as we can apply these tools to any area of our lives. We have the ability to say, "Enough is enough; I choose this instead." At such a time, your power is expanding.

"Every decision you make—every decision—is not a decision about what to do. It's a decision about who you are. When you see this, when you understand it, everything changes. You begin to see life in a new way. All events, occurrences, and situations turn into opportunities to do what you came here to do."

—Neale Donald Walsch,
author, *Conversations with God*

Win or Die

Years ago, I read a story about a military leader who led a group of soldiers during an invasion of an island. They were severely outnumbered. The leader made a decision to burn their boats to eliminate any possible way to retreat (commitment). As the boats lit up in flames, he pointed out to his men that turning back was no longer an option and retreat was not possible. He told them, "We either win or we die." In essence, he reduced their possible decisions to two: win or die. They decided to live, so that day, while being significantly outnumbered, they won. There is power in decision! What decisions do you need to make and what decisions are you willing to make?

The Power of a Good Decision

We are going to talk about some great concepts that have truly helped me, just as they have helped hundreds and even thousands of people who apply these ideas in their lives. I can brag about these ideas because most of them are not mine. I compiled these notions, then I applied them, and they all were beneficial. You can now do the same. In your case, these powerful ideas are all in this book. My hope is that you will apply these ideas and that you too will gain great benefits from them.

As splendid as these ideas are, if you don't make the all-important decision to use and apply them, they cannot help you. I realize that most of these strategies require a lot of commitment and time. This process is not a quick fix or a magic pill, but these ideas do work over a period of time. This is a normal part of the reconditioning process. You didn't develop your bad habits in one day, and you won't develop good habits in one day either.

I know the power of a decision and how it can make a huge difference in our lives, provided it is an empowering decision. Depending on what it is, that decision could start a positive process instantaneously versus having to go through weeks, months, or even years to accomplish the same thing. **Decision is powerful.** Many of the ideas presented here are interrelated, and, to keep focused and on track, I will be discussing them one at a time to keep this dialogue as simple as possible.

Small Decisions Are Big Decisions

The most critical decisions might not necessarily be the big decisions. Many people, myself included, sometimes put too much emphasis on "big" decisions, when our success in this life depends on the little decisions we are making all day long, every day of our lives.

These everyday decisions are like tiny insects that can bring down a mighty tree. After withstanding hundreds of years of fires, storms, and wind, which are all big challenges, the mighty tree falls at the teeth of a tiny bug and a bunch of his friends. These everyday decisions form habits, which shape our character and determine our destiny. We make decisions constantly. Of course, we are also on autopilot. Every day, we have the ability to veto a decision and change direction. We may not be able to achieve a new destination overnight, but we can certainly point ourselves in that direction.

Repeated Continually, Small Decisions Form Our Lives

Beware of all your decisions, especially the small decisions. For instance, it may be a challenge to understand the ramifications of a smile to a stranger or holding the door for someone or letting someone cut in during busy traffic. It may be difficult to understand the ramifications of not kissing your loved ones before you leave or a hug you didn't give or a deep breath you didn't take. It might not be obvious at first if we skip going for a walk or avoid taking a yoga class or don't stop after the second glass of wine.

These decisions may not seem like monumental, life-changing issues. However, they are part of the essence of life. These little decisions may not make a big difference in one day, but when these same small decisions are made repeatedly for a month, a year, or a lifetime, they shape and form our lives.

What you may not have realized until now is that every day you are making or failing to make certain "small" decisions that will ultimately have a huge impact on your life. It all starts with these little decisions. When you become more aware of your thoughts and environment, you will make all these important decisions in a fashion that propels you toward your target.

Pay Attention to Your Decisions

The intent of this chapter is to remind you of the power of decision and also to increase your understanding of the importance of all the decisions we make. Most of them will impact your ideal body in some fashion. Most importantly, it will be necessary for you to make some decisions to help improve your life and take more facets of your life to the next level. Please don't fret at the idea that you have so many new decisions to make, because you are already making them.

Now your responsibility is to pay more attention to those decisions. If you are not sure what the future ramifications of your decisions are, you may want to "future pace" your decisions. This is a great activity.

List all the decisions you make in a day and categorize them as physical, mental, financial, spiritual, and relational. Now you can "future pace" them. You ask yourself honestly, "If I keep making this decision every day, where will I be in one year? Where will I be in five years? In twenty years? What about in my lifetime?"

Have you ever wished for a crystal ball so that you could see into your future? This concept is not quite like having a crystal ball. However, it could be comparable to what you might see if you had one. This approach might be the closest thing you will get to a crystal ball. If you don't like what you see, then you have another decision to make. Do you want to stay on this track, heading toward that target, or is it time to change directions or change tracks?

Perhaps this exercise will cause you to make a big decision, but remember that they are all big decisions over time. "Future pace" every area of your life, and you will have a new understanding of the weight and power of each little daily choice and how it can affect your life. I share this concept with you so that you can take the reins of your life and control what train and tracks you are traveling on. Where you go and how you get there are up to you and your decisions.

TEACHING POINTS

- ☑ Making a decision gathers the power of the universe.
- ☑ When the WHY is big enough, the decision is easy.
- ☑ Making a decision is powerful.
- ☑ Some decisions can mean life or death.
- ☑ Small decisions are big decisions.
- ☑ Pay attention to all of your decisions.

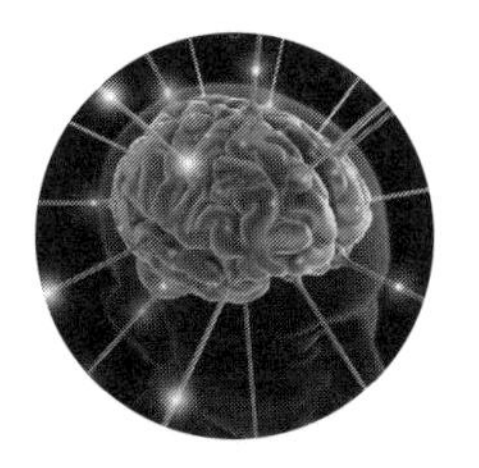

CHAPTER 9

Belief

"If one advances confidently in the direction of one's dreams, and endeavors to live the life which one has imagined, one will meet with a success unexpected in common hours."

—Henry David Thoreau

What Is a Belief?

A belief is a thought repeated over time, and a thought repeated on multiple occasions becomes a belief. There are many theories as to what others think a thought is. Hence, you will find many definitions for the word "thought." This topic could easily be a book in itself. For our purpose, **let us describe a thought as a neural net of cells in the brain.** When these cells are reinforced by repeating the thoughts or by adding emotions to a thought, they strengthen to a point that makes thinking that thought (now a belief) much easier to do. Once that thought is initiated, it begins to fire the rest of the way or is completed automatically.

The bottom line is: If you repeat (think) a thought enough times, you begin to believe it. Eventually, it becomes a "natural" part of you. It becomes your belief. It does not matter what the thought is. It could be a good thought or a bad thought, a positive or negative thought, or anything in between. **All that matters is that the neural nets or groups of cells get reinforced multiple times.**

To create your ideal body, you will take advantage of this same process. Many times, you will repeat the thoughts you now choose to transform into beliefs. **The strength of a belief is built by repetition and protein.** Protein, you ask? Yes. We speed up the process of strengthening the neural net by adding emotion to the thought. Emotion releases proteins at the synaptic gaps, thus "bonding" the cells together. This chemical activity, in essence, creates a belief.

How Are Beliefs Formed?

We inherit genes from our parents. Among these "gifts" are certain physical and mental characteristics. Because our parents give us our physical makeup from their physical makeup, it would seem sensible to consider the possibility that they could have passed on to us certain beliefs and propensities. I believe our genes play a role in our behavior. However, I also believe our environment can play an even bigger role. Here's the good and bad news: **we can be conditioned to believe.** Think about it. The chances are good that, if you were raised Christian, you were raised to believe in Santa Claus. I'm not talking about the Spirit of St. Nick but the character who flies around the planet with the sleigh full of toys pulled by eight magical reindeer. The one who delivers toys to every good girl and boy on Christmas Eve. In fact, even if you are not Christian, you still may have been raised to believe in Santa Claus.

Why did we believe? First, we were small children and very impressionable. Second, we were told this idea by sources we trusted and believed. Third, this information was told to us repeatedly. Eventually, we were conditioned to believe Santa Claus existed.

Because this conditioning started at the time we were small children, this process of "brainwashing" or conditioning was easily and quickly accomplished. This is a good example everyone can relate to.

The process of conditioning begins in childhood, but it doesn't stop there. Adults are conditioned as well. Kids just have to make up their minds, while adults have to change their minds. This example is not limited to religion. If a family raising a child is bilingual, the child will have a high probability of being bilingual. If a family speaks three languages, then the child is likely to speak three languages. If a family speaks one language, chances are the child will speak only one language. Our environment shapes our programming, and our programming forms our beliefs. Our beliefs determine our results and our successes. If your current results are less than desirable, you might consider changing your beliefs. You can achieve a transformation by altering your programming and upgrading your environment. We will cover these concepts later.

With repetition, our conscious thoughts help form our beliefs, which direct our subconscious thoughts, which govern our actions. Our repeated actions form our habits. Our habits shape our character, and our character determines our destiny.

With repetition, our conscious thoughts help form our beliefs, which direct our subconscious thoughts, which govern our actions. Our repeated actions form our habits. Our habits shape our character, and our character determines our destiny.

Beliefs Control Our Thoughts and Actions

Think of your beliefs as an operating system similar to the operating system on your computer. If your computer has a faulty program, the entire system will reflect that. If you want to run the latest updates, you have to install them on your operating system. You also may have to uninstall previous programs before you can upgrade. Similarly, if you do not upgrade, you are essentially stuck with the old abilities. When you update your old beliefs, you'll update your operating system, which allows you to use a new collection of possibilities.

When my computer acts up, I do what little I know to do. I am not a computer expert, so if it crashes, I simply reboot. Then, hopefully, it will work properly again and I can go back to what I was doing. If the hardware of the computer—the CPU, monitor, keyboard, and mouse—work fine, then it must be a software issue. However, situations occur when you need a computer expert to overhaul the system.

Similar to software, our beliefs "run" our health and fitness, and they determine whether we possess our ideal bodies. Our beliefs are internal and are housed in the subconscious mind. Unfortunately, we have yet to determine where the "reset button" is for the subconscious mind. However, those beliefs *can* be "reset." It just requires a little more effort than it does to reset a computer.

By light years, the human mind exceeds computers in complexity. Nevertheless, we can reset our own programming. You simply need to learn how to make this happen. We will talk more about resetting or retraining our minds in the section on the reconditioning process.

It doesn't matter whether or not one accepts that beliefs are running his or her programs. Beliefs do run our programs, and they will continue to run them. The question one needs to ask oneself is "Are my current beliefs serving me? If the answer is no, then the next question is "Do I want to change them?"

Several years ago, when I was "failing" to exercise consistently, I didn't believe I could keep to a routine, because I didn't understand the habit-forming process. When I first began to try to exercise and I stopped, I didn't know why I had stopped. At this point, I became discouraged and I thought failure must be normal. However, something within me did not want to give up, so I looked for role models.

Sadly, I did not see anyone else succeeding at exercising consistently. Most people were failing. Even today, as more people are getting involved with exercise, there is still only a small percentage of the population that exercises on a regular basis. When I saw everyone else failing, I realized that falling off the exercise wagon actually was the norm. Now, **I have finally learned that it does not have to be normal for people to cease doing what they really need or want to do.** That is the purpose of this book. As you read and apply the suggestions presented here, you will soon experience a new norm, and that the new norm can be consistent exercise, if you choose it.

Let's discuss a few important points about beliefs:

- They run your personal "software" program.
- You have them whether or not you think so.
- They can be altered.

Any Idea Can Become a Belief

Whether something is true at the present time or is a downright lie, it can be programmed into our minds. We can be taught to believe anything. Why is that important? You can "teach" yourself to believe. **When you believe, you can achieve the goal you are striving for. When you believe it, you will achieve it.**

Centuries ago, people believed that the sun revolved around the earth, and that is what they taught their children. There was a time when people were sentenced to death for even suggesting that this belief was not true. Some sources suggest that early in the year 1600, Giordano Bruno, philosopher, mathematician, and astronomer, was burned at the stake because he refused to recant his position that the sun did not revolve around the earth. We also used to believe the earth was flat. What else do we believe right now that may not be true?

If you are told something enough times, more than likely, you'll believe it. As you grew up and you began to think for yourself, you started to challenge some of those beliefs. We can look at all religions. If a child is born into a particular family that practices a certain religion, there is a high likelihood that the child participates in the same religion. Children generally seem to practice the religion of their parents because they have been conditioned to believe in that religion. Take that same child at a very early age and extract him or her from that family practicing religion "X" and put him or her with a family that practices religion "Y." After some time and conditioning, that same child will probably practice religion "Y" instead. It doesn't matter what religions X or Y represent. What matters is the conditioning the child is subject to. Whatever thought (or idea) is repeated over and over becomes a belief.

Could a Pep Talk Change a Belief?

I am not sure exactly how many motivational "talks" I received as a youngster. I don't recall too many. The first motivational talk I do remember hearing was from my cousin Bob Sanch, Jr. This pep talk took place during my late teens. I'm fairly sure that, at the time, Bob didn't realize the magnitude of the words he shared with me on that day. Occasionally, I remind Bob and thank him for guiding me along my path. At the time, he was actually helping me with my bowling game. However, everything affects everything else. I was experiencing some challenges improving my game, and I expressed my frustration to Bob. What he shared with me during that pep talk helped me change not only my bowling game but my life!

I was bowling in a practice session, as I did most days. I loved bowling, and my goal was to improve my technique. Bob was a very good bowler and a good bowling mentor. From time to time, he shared specific tips with me on how to improve.

That day, we talked about mindset. He used a certain professional bowler at the time to illustrate his point. This pro bowler had personality, and Bob used the word "cocky" to describe the pro's attitude, which I understood. Bob also talked about other professionals in other sports who were at the top of their games.

My cousin explained how each of these professionals possessed a common trait. They all believed in themselves. That is why they exuded so much confidence. Each of these highly ranked individuals acquired a belief within himself. This belief was about each one's superb capacity for winning. That belief was an idea that each one accepted, and, hence, their performances mirrored those beliefs.

Although it may have lasted only five to ten minutes, that conversation got me thinking differently. I began to believe in myself and in my ability as a bowler. Actually, the physical aspects of bowling were not my concern. Remember, I practiced almost every day. However, I was still lacking in the mental and spiritual side of the game, and my thoughts and feelings were not aligned with my actions.

Then, I began to believe in myself. I made progress, but it was slow going. Bob had not taught me the specific steps to enable me to believe in myself. I had to figure those out on my own. What he did share, however, was powerful enough to move me to the next level of my understanding and awareness. This involved not only the game of bowling but the game of life as well. For that guidance, I am very grateful.

Once I began to believe in myself, there was a shift. At first, it wasn't a big shift, but I did get onto a different mental train and began to move in a different direction. The power of the right belief can make a world of difference. My bowling scores improved, and my bowling average went up. As a bonus, my life began improving too.

Beliefs CAN Be Altered

Years later, when I created a new belief system and understood that I could be fit and healthy and possess the body of my dreams, I picked myself up, dusted myself off (from twenty years of on-again, off-again failure), and began my new exercise program. In over **four years**, I have not missed a single day. Coming from a twenty-year history of sporadic exercise consistency at best, this was a breakthrough of monumental proportions. It happened for me, and it can happen for you when you apply the ideas presented in this book.

I created a consistent exercise program that has not only changed my life but has transformed it. The Don Staley I was four years earlier is a completely different person from the man I am today. I dropped over thirty pounds, and that is the least of the benefits I now enjoy! The confidence and power I gained—not only physically, but mentally and spiritually, as well—are beyond what I ever imagined or expected. We are all changing on a daily basis. Every one of us is continuously changing, whether we notice it or not. To me, these types of changes were like a quantum leap, a huge jump in improvement, and it keeps getting better.

It is important to realize that nothing really changed except my understanding and belief in myself and, of course, my taking action. A powerful new understanding helped me believe in something that had eluded me for over twenty years. You may be wondering how to change your beliefs, and we will talk about that in great detail as we discuss the reconditioning process. For now, a general overview about belief will suffice to get you moving in a new direction.

Later, we will go into great detail about exactly how you can condition or reprogram yourself to believe. Again, **a belief is a thought you have "thought" repeatedly.** The neural net of brain cells fires again and again every time we think a particular thought, and every time a particular thought is "fired," it becomes stronger.

Once you believe, you can achieve your desire, and even if that process takes some time, you *will* achieve it.

You Can Alter Your Beliefs

An important truth about beliefs is that they can be changed, altered, and rewritten. We are not stuck with our old beliefs if we don't choose to be. Before I became aware of this concept, I didn't believe I was a good bowler, I didn't believe that I could enjoy having the body of my dreams, and I didn't believe I could maintain a consistent exercise program to acquire and keep my ideal body. When I changed my beliefs regarding those areas of my life, regardless of whether it was consciously or accidentally, my life was altered. You too can change your beliefs. If you can read this book, you can change your beliefs.

Changing My Beliefs Achieved My Goals

Before I "retired" from bowling, because I had upgraded my beliefs, I qualified and played for my college bowling team and carried an average of well over 200. Once I began exercising consistently every day, I shed over thirty pounds, reduced my waist size by several inches, and reached my objective of having my ideal body.

Perhaps I do not exercise every day as intensely as Lance Armstrong, but my intention is not to compete in the Tour de France. Every day, I continue to improve on my ideal body, even though I have reached the original objectives I set out to achieve. These goals were accomplished after I changed my beliefs about these things. You too can accomplish your dream, and when you do, you can set new targets. Certainly, I have set new goals, new levels to strive for, and I will continue to improve.

Anthony Robbins, another mentor, introduced me to CANI (constant and never-ending improvement), which is a great concept. My version of this ancient idea, which is based on the latest brain research that our subconscious mind doesn't recognize a negative, is constant perpetual improvement (CPI). CPI is stated in the positive, which the mind recognizes. Interestingly, your subconscious mind does not recognize a negative. If I ask you not to think of a purple cow, what will you think about in your attempt NOT to think about it? Yes, you will be thinking of a purple cow, and you will actually see it in your mind's eye. Therefore, *I* believe that it is better to focus on the positive and avoid the negative.

Your current results are the effects of your previous and current beliefs. If you are wondering about your beliefs, ask yourself these questions:

1. Are my current beliefs bringing me closer to my objective or moving me away?
2. What beliefs would I need to "own" to accomplish my intention of having my ideal body?

Your answers to those questions will help guide and show you what you need to do regarding your beliefs. Your answers will also point to the gap between where you are and where you need to be to accomplish your new target.

Even as powerful as beliefs are, you will still need to make a *commitment* to yourself and to your target objective. It is essential to understand that beliefs are important, and it is also critical that you believe you will accomplish your objective or target. If you are not there yet, you must strive to attain that level of knowing. Do whatever it takes to convince yourself. We will talk more about that in the section on awareness. Remember that belief is a starting point. You will raise the bar as we go, but you must first get yourself to the point of belief, which will be described in the section on reprogramming.

> "All truth passes through three stages. First, it is ridiculed. Second, it is violently opposed. Third, it is accepted as being self-evident."
>
> **—Arthur Schopenhauer**

Three Beliefs You Must Develop

To wrap up this chapter, it is important to note that there are three main beliefs you must develop to achieve your desires. These beliefs can start from nothing. They can start from the simple desire to have, be, or do more. You can do it. **You must believe in yourself and your dream, and you must believe you can achieve your dream.** It is not critical that you believe in this concept at first, because you can reprogram yourself to believe. What is important is you can eventually get yourself to believe. **When you believe, you ACHIEVE!**

TEACHING POINTS

- ☑ Beliefs are simply thoughts that have been repeated.
- ☑ Beliefs control our actions and long-term behaviors.
- ☑ Beliefs are formed by genetics and conditioning (repetition of thoughts and/or emotions).
- ☑ Lies and myths can become beliefs. Any idea can become a belief.
- ☑ Old beliefs can be changed. Just as old conditioning was installed, so can new conditioning replace it.
- ☑ You can change beliefs by conditioning or reprogramming.
- ☑ Changing beliefs changes your results.
- ☑ Three beliefs you must develop:
  1. Believe your dream is obtainable by you.
  2. Believe in your dream.
  3. Believe in yourself.

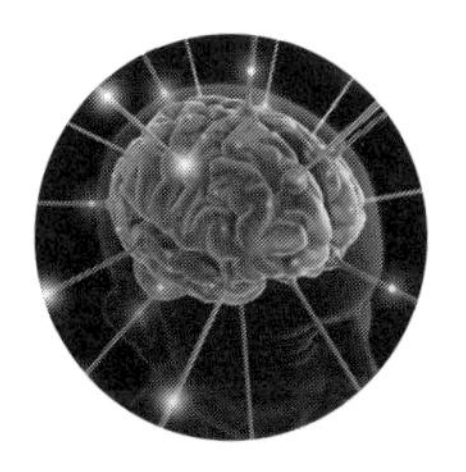

CHAPTER 10

Commitment

"Wheresoever you go, go with all your heart."

—Confucius

The next step in this process is to **commit yourself to achieving your ideal body, to completely commit to your target or objective.** This means **you must also commit to the reconditioning process.** You may be thinking "What is the difference between decision and commitment?" A decision is when you make a choice to do it—whatever "it" may be. You have come to a resolution of what it is you want. On the other hand, a commitment is the decision to stick to the process of achieving the objective. The decision gets you going, and the commitment keeps you going.

Obstacles Are Good

Obstacles are normal elements of living. Everyone on the planet encounters obstacles. Obstacles help us to learn and grow. They are good, and we need them. Obstacles mimic the headwind for the sailboat or the weights for the bodybuilder. Overcoming obstacles ultimately makes us smarter and stronger. Although such hindrances may not appear to do so, they help propel us toward our objectives.

However, there will be some obstacles that seem bigger than others. When they show up on our doorsteps and we are not prepared—or if we are not committed to reaching our goals—chances are we will falter. If we are not committed, we are likely to surrender our objectives to the obstacles because the obstacles may appear insurmountable. At such a time, we stop striving toward our dreams. Nevertheless, when we *are* committed, we do whatever it takes to win out. With commitment, we can accomplish our objectives—no matter how big the obstacles.

> "If you are only interested, you will only do what is convenient, but if you are committed you will do whatever it takes."
>
> **—John Assaraf, *New York Times* bestselling author**

Commit or Lose

This idea of commitment has made a world of difference for me and my successes. I have found that when you strive for a big objective, there are times when the opportunity to do what is convenient appears. In such instances, your level of commitment is tested. You may find out whether you truly want or desire your objective. Will you choose to strive toward your objective over the obstacles you need to overcome, or will you choose the easy path, which is convenient? When you're committed, those obstacles give way. They dissolve in front of you and yield to your objective as well as to your determination. If you are not committed, you are fighting a losing battle. Are you committed to your objective?

How Committed Are You?

A few years ago, a rock climber in Colorado named Aron Ralston was ascending alone, got his arm caught in some rocks, and became trapped. He was destined to die unless someone else happened to come by to save him. Unfortunately, he was out in the wilderness and chances were slim anyone would find him. After a few days, he ran out of food and water, and it looked as if all hope was lost. He made the decision to live, and to do so, he knew he had to cut off his arm. Fortunately, this is a decision most of us will never have to make.

After Aron made that decision, he then needed to execute it. This is where the commitment comes in. **It is one thing to know what you need to do, but it is another issue to actually do it.** Aron needed to take steps that would make the toughest among us queasy. First, he had to break his own arm, which seems crazy enough. Then, he had to cut his arm off with a dull knife. He sawed on his own arm with his little pocket knife until he was free. After all that, he still needed to trek back to civilization to procure the medical help he needed. He was committed!

Of course, this is an extreme example, yet it does illustrate the point perfectly: it is one thing to decide on what you want; it's another to commit to actually doing it. Are you committed?

Are you willing to do whatever it takes to reach your objective? Would you cut your arm off to save your life? These are interesting questions, and your answers reveal your true level of commitment. Your answers are your actions, and your actions show how committed you are. What actions are you taking? What actions do you need to take?

"Until one is committed, there is hesitancy, the chance to draw back, always ineffectiveness. Concerning all acts of initiative (and creation), there is one elementary truth, the ignorance of which kills countless ideas and splendid plans: that the moment one definitely commits oneself, then providence moves too."

—W. H. Murray, from *The Scottish Himalayan Expedition*

You Will Be Tested

I can recall many times when my commitment was tested, especially in the first part of the process. The beginning of your reconditioning process is critical. As you begin to create a new habit or lifestyle, you are stepping out of your comfort zone. Remember from chapter 2 that your amygdala, a part of your brain, sends out stress chemicals into your body, which makes you feel doubt, fear, and anxiety. These chemicals make us feel uncomfortable in order to bring us back to safety. The amygdala is the emotional part of the brain, and one of its main functions is keeping us safe. The brain is working to maintain homeostasis, and when the outside world starts looking different from the inside world, the brain releases certain chemicals in an attempt to get the body back to safety.

Early into the program, when I began exercising on a daily basis, I became ill. It was nothing major, just a good old-fashioned cold with a bit of nausea. However, years earlier, I was taught that the body needed rest, which is somewhat true, as the body does need rest. In the past, when exercising, if I ever experienced a cold or flu, I took two or three days off to give my body the rest it "needed." When I encountered this obstacle after having made a commitment, I had a decision to make. However, this decision would be based on the new information I had obtained.

One very critical point is to establish a habit of consistency; action must be taken toward our new habit *every single day*. The brain needs a certain amount of time and repetition to create habits. In 2006, I heard about an experiment[1] with convex goggles conducted by NASA. According to my mentor, they were looking to test certain effects of disorientation on the astronaut's body. Therefore, NASA had astronauts wear convex goggles, which turned everything they saw upside down. They were instructed to wear theses goggles 24/7 for a period of time.

The scientists conducting the experiments discovered a few things that weren't at all what they were looking for. First, they found that within three to four weeks of the experiments, some of the candidates' brains "flipped" the images they were seeing back to normal. Their brains began to turn everything they saw back right-side-up; they began to see "normally" while still wearing the goggles! The second thing they stumbled on was that if a candidate took off the googles after this "flipping" point, he or she would see everything upside down until his or her brain rewired itself back to normal. The third major discovery they made was that if the candidate took off the googles any time before the flipping point, he or she would have to begin again at day one. It appeared that it took about thirty days for this rewiring to take hold.

[1] *At the time of this printing, my research team and I have not been able to track down this experiment to confirm the validity of these results or even the experiment's existence. Please let me know If you have any information.*

Certainly I knew that if I missed one day, I would have to begin again at day one. I didn't want to start over, so on this particular day, I got onto the treadmill and completed my walk for the day, even though I didn't feel up to it. Frankly, it was the last thing I wanted to do that day. My commitment level was tested, and I met the challenge. Interestingly, after I passed that test, a new confidence enveloped me. I thought that if I could exercise when I wasn't 100% healthy, I could do it any time.

It wasn't long before my commitment was tested again. A week or two later, I had an extremely busy day. Eleven o'clock p.m. rolled around, and I realized that I hadn't done my exercise for the day. At that point, I was exhausted and ready for bed. Believe me when I say exercise was the last thing I wanted to do. Certainly it would have been easy to "rational-lies" my way out of it. Any reasonable person looking at my situation would have understood and let me off the hook for the day. Fortunately for me, the responsibility lay in *my* hands. I wasn't reasonable. I was committed! After going through a couple of quick mental processes, which we will talk about in the reprogramming section, I prepared myself, walked into my home gym, and completed a decent workout.

Would I have won any awards that night for my level of exercise intensity? I doubt it. However, I did earn another triumph over laziness, reasonableness, and my old conditioning. I conquered another obstacle. I also gained a new understanding of how the proper strategies, backed by commitment and executed with action, can propel me toward any objective. This new understanding even shot down a previously misguided belief that exercise consistency was impossible. That old belief was finally destroyed after failing at it for twenty years. Remember, the past does NOT equal the future.

Passing the Test Builds a Different Muscle

Your commitment will be tested! You either pass or you fail. However, you always learn, so failure is an illusion. Sometimes, you realize that you need to relearn the lesson of what commitment is. You are either committed to achieve your objective or you are only interested. Which are you? Are you committed, or are you only interested?

Every time you are tested and you work through the situation, you develop a muscle. This is not a muscle in your body, although that could be a side effect. Instead, **it is a muscle of confidence, commitment, and will.** It is not just about willpower, as we will discuss, although you will definitely need willpower to get the habit-creation process started.

It is important to note that it would have been easy to NOT exercise on those days I have been discussing. There were plenty of days during which I was tested, and each time it did get easier, as I became mentally stronger.

I think one of the things that many personal development books and programs miss is a healthy discussion on encountering obstacles. I believe that if you know obstacles are ahead, you can be ready to handle them. Your managing of obstacles will dissolve their power and increase your power. Also, to a certain extent, the element of surprise is eliminated. Personally, I don’t want to remain focused on obstacles because I don't want to give them energy. However, when you are aware of what they are, you won’t be surprised when they show up. Spend most of your time looking for solutions, and answers will emerge.

To predict exactly when and where these obstacles will appear for each individual is beyond the scope of this book, even if that could ever be determined. By no means am I saying that your obstacles will be like mine. Everyone is starting from a different level, so every obstacle has the potential to vary somewhat.

Sometimes, You May Need to Become Resourceful

I remember another time, when my wife was out of town and I was caring for our son, who was two years old at the time. For me to walk on the treadmill uninterrupted for thirty to forty minutes and expect my son to sit still did not appear to be the best plan. Instead, I bundled him up like a little Eskimo and we ventured outside for a walk. I exercised that day by pushing him in a stroller and keeping him involved. Likewise, you will encounter times when resourcefulness is necessary. When you become open to universal intelligence, the ideas or solutions you need to keep you on track are likely to appear. Tapping into your intuition is a reliable source and a wise guide.

Once you make the decision to take aim at a certain goal, you then need to commit to this objective as a heat-seeking missile locks on to its target.

A special point to make here is that an intelligent missile is usually preprogrammed to hit a target. Depending on the level of sophistication of the missile, it may be reprogrammed during flight to a new mark before it hits the original target. No matter how much technology improves from its present state, I doubt there will ever be a missile as sophisticated or as complex as a human being's mind. The human mind develops that missile, not the other way around. We are powerful!

No matter what target you may be locked on to or where you are heading, you can take the controls and reprogram your mind with a new target. Depending on where you are, you may need to act fast, because you may not have much time. Make the decision and commit to it! When you apply the ideas available in the remainder of this book, you can lock on to a new target. Once you have chosen your target and committed to it, you will accomplish your objective if and when you reprogram or retrain yourself and take the appropriate actions. None of the strategies and knowledge covered here will be worth anything unless you TAKE ACTION!

TEACHING POINTS

- ☑ Obstacles are good.
- ☑ You either commit or you lose.
- ☑ Do you know how committed you are?
- ☑ Your actions are the reflections of your level of commitment.
- ☑ Your commitment level will be tested.
- ☑ Every success builds your "muscle."
- ☑ Resourcefulness is your ally.

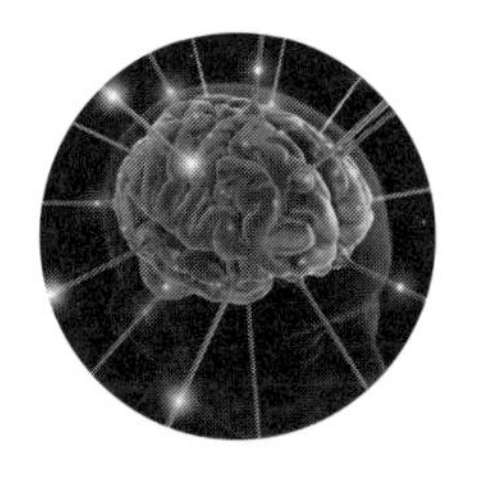

CHAPTER 11

Action

"Great acts are made up of small deeds."

—Lao Tzu

There are two major types of action that are essential for your success. The critical and most often neglected action in numerous personal development books and programs is the action of **reprogramming the mind to create long-term habits**. The second type required for success is the **achieving type of action**—the actual deeds or behaviors that you are striving to incorporate into your life. Many times, the emphasis is placed on the actual activity, but unless this action is programmed into the mind as a new habit or belief, it will only be a temporary action and will be neglected when an obstacle surfaces or when your mood changes.

Going through the personal development process includes learning, growing, and reprogramming the mind. The action of achieving requires the movement toward achieving your objective. Examples of achieving actions are exercising to achieve your ideal body or eating nutritious foods to achieve good health. Not eating unhealthy foods is also an achieving action. As you go through the entire process of creating your ideal body, keep in mind these two types of actions: reprogramming and achieving.

It has been my experience that most people focus on the achieving actions, but they quit before a habit is formed. The reprogramming actions help install the proper mental conditioning to ensure that a habit is created, which ensures long-term success. We will talk more about reprogramming in an upcoming chapter.

You Are Worthy and We Need You

If I may insert a little plug for you, one reason I feel you should make that commitment and take action is that the world needs you; I believe you are unique. Planet Earth currently provides a home for approximately 6.5 billion people, not to mention all those who lived here before us. Even with those incomprehensible numbers, we are all unique. I have a saying that expresses each individual's uniqueness: "everyone is a snowflake." I derived this from the thought that every snowflake is unique. You are you, and no one is exactly like you. There never has been and never will be anyone precisely like you.

No two dreams are exactly the same. Even though your dream may appear to be similar to the dream of another, you are the reason your dream is different. You are the only one who can achieve this dream from your perspective. No one else will ever fulfill your dream. They can achieve a similar goal from their perspective but never your own unique dream.

You possess a specific desire or a particular dream for a reason. You can achieve it, and as you strive for and accomplish your dream, the world grows. The world becomes a better place.

There is only one chance for your dream to be accomplished. It can be completed only by you, and it can only be fulfilled in your lifetime and only if you take action. **That lifetime is now, and now is the time!** This is exactly why you must take action and you must do so now!

You are reading these words now for a reason. As I write these words and you read them, we each have a purpose. No one purpose is greater than another. We are all adding to this canvas of life. We each hold a paintbrush. What are you going to paint on this masterpiece? You can choose your purpose! Take a chance on you as I took a chance on me and put your paint brush deliberately on the canvas of life. Help us create a masterpiece.

Actually, you already are crafting your special work, and now you can decide exactly how you will appear on this painting. Make a commitment to this idea that you have been longing to achieve, and when you back it up with action and the reprogramming we'll talk about, you'll be living a life with so much more joy and happiness. You will really be *living* life, perhaps, for the very first time.

"Every man dies. Not every man truly lives."

—William Wallace, *Braveheart*

Reprogramming New Habits Is a Process

Years ago, I first encountered portions of the reprogramming process in two books, *Think and Grow Rich* by Napoleon Hill and *See You at the Top* by Zig Ziglar. Both of these authors introduced me to the concept of reprogramming the subconscious mind. I am grateful for these important teachers, as I am grateful for all those who have shined light on my path along the way. Maybe, when I first read these ideas, I wasn't ready. For whatever reason, this concept finally hit me years later when John Assaraf explained it to me, along with some of the latest research, at a mindset conference in San Diego in October of 2006.

Reprogramming the mind does not happen in a seminar or at a weekend program, although great progress can be made during these types of programs. **Reprogramming the mind is a process, and it requires consistent effort over time to undo the programming your mind endured for possibly several decades.** We have been thinking and living a certain way for many years. To overturn our old programming and rewrite that script initially requires time and a lot of effort. Once you install habits of the reprogramming process, it becomes automatic. Then, it is only a matter of time before you reprogram yourself to accomplish your objectives and to hit your target. Patience is going to be required, as well as persistence, and when you stick with it, you will be greatly rewarded.

The human brain is a complex and amazing part of our equally remarkable human body. As we discussed earlier, our brain is not our mind. Some people confuse the two, although the brain remains a part of the mind. The brain exists as a physical organ, the hardware. The mind exists as the activity, similar to software. Humans are significantly more complex than a mere computer, but this comparison gives you at least some basis from which to compare. The mind lies in the brain but is not limited to the brain.

In fact, the mind is not limited to the body either. It could take an entire book to explain just that concept and still there would be questions. I know that concept may be far-reaching for some. However, there is a lot more going on than what you can observe with your physical senses.

Just Because You Do Not See It Does Not Mean It Isn't There

Years ago, if we wanted to lock our car door, we locked it before we closed the door by pressing the lock inside the car, or we would physically stick the key in the door lock and turn the key. Now, almost all cars made today come standard with remote door locks. You can lock or unlock your door by pressing a simple button on your key or keychain. How does pressing a button lock or unlock a car door? By pressing a button, you can even open a car door or trunk using wireless technology. Do you see or hear anything during this process? I'm not talking about the sound of the actual locking or unlocking or the car alarm's beeping. Do you hear or see the radio wave signal being sent from the keychain to the door lock or alarm? The answer is no. You do not see it because it happens beyond the range of our physical senses.

The keychain is sending radio waves, which vibrate at different light waves than we can see with our eyes. We do not see anything come out of the keychain, but we understand that a signal is being sent. We also understand that a signal is being received by either the lock or alarm. Even though you cannot see what is happening, you understand that something *is* happening. We don't see the radio waves because they are being transmitted beyond our scope of vision.

Our Physical Senses Are Limited

Our human ability allows us to hear a certain range of frequencies, which are between approximately 15 hertz and 20,000 hertz. Any sounds above or below those frequencies go unnoticed by humans. Our sight is also limited to a narrow band of light wavelengths of approximately 400 nm (nanometers) to 700 nm. Any light that occurs above or below those frequencies or wavelengths goes unseen by our physical senses. It is important to realize that there is a lot happening outside of the range of our senses.

We are brought up to depend on our five physical senses, but there is so much more going on than what we can perceive with those limited five senses of sight, sound, taste, touch, and smell.

Not able to see	Able to see	Not able to see
radio waves, microwaves, infrared	visible to humans	ultraviolet, X-rays, gamma
< 399 nm	400 nm to 700 nm	> 701 nm
Not able to hear	**Able to hear**	**Not able to hear**
< 15 Hz	15 to 20,000 Hz	> 20,000 Hz

We can see only a certain range of wavelengths. If the wavelength of light at which we are looking is out of our range of vision, we will not be able to see it. The same is true with sound. We hear only within a certain range. Have you ever heard a dog whistle? Neither have I. Dogs can hear it because they have a hearing capacity that exceeds ours. Dogs can hear what we cannot, but dogs don't hear everything either. A bat has a greater capacity to hear than a dog. A dog can hear from 40 Hz to approximately 65,000 Hz, and a bat can hear from 10 Hz to 100,000 Hz.

Why is all this information important? It is included here to illustrate the point that **things are happening all the time, and we may not be consciously aware of everything because many things occur beyond the grasp of our physical senses.** Scientists say the brain takes in billions of bits of information every second and we are only consciously aware of about two thousand bits per second. Most of that information pertains to our environment and reaches us through our limited five senses.

Things are happening all the time, and we may not be consciously aware of everything because many things occur beyond the grasp of our physical senses.

Our incredible brains filter out most of the information we are exposed to and thankfully so. Could you imagine trying to process billions of bits of information in addition to running our entire bodies? No thanks. The point is that there is a lot more than what meets the eye or ear—a lot more. There is much more going on around us than our five senses tell us.

Programs Are Always Running

There's a lot going on that we are not aware of. How does that fact relate to the reprogramming process? It is important for you to understand that programs are already installed on your human software that run different aspects of your life. For instance, you may have a program running that keeps you overweight, fat, and out of shape. This program overrides any temporary, conscious thought to become healthy and get into shape.

Remember, until it is overwritten, the subconscious is more powerful long-term than the conscious mind.

Using Autopilot Is Easier than Flying Manually

Imagine a sophisticated aircraft and a knowledgeable pilot. The pilot represents the conscious mind. The plane's computer and autopilot represent the subconscious mind. Let's begin this example in mid-flight, as we are in some aspect of the mid-flight of our lives.

The pilot wants to go in an entirely new direction. If the pilot is experienced, he or she knows how to reset or reprogram the autopilot. After the pilot resets the program, the plane will turn in the new direction, toward the newly programmed destination. Once the program is changed, the aircraft will accomplish this automatically. Consider this same example with an inexperienced pilot or copilot who does not know about the autopilot system and wants to go in a new direction.

Because this pilot does not know how to reprogram the autopilot, he or she may try to steer the plane manually by grabbing the yoke or steering wheel and turning it to go in the new direction. The plane will turn according to the physical effort of the pilot and head in the direction of the new goal. However, because the new destination isn't programmed into the plane's computer, the new copilot must take hold of the controls and manually steer the plane. Unless he or she reprograms the autopilot, the copilot will need to continue to exert unnecessary effort to manually control the plane to the new destination.

Working Harder Is NOT the Answer

However, with our personal, human autopilot system, if we don't reprogram new destinations into our minds, a lot of effort is required to manually steer our lives to new directions. When we "let go of the controls" before a new program is installed, we will always revert back to our former programming. Unlike most modern aircraft autopilot systems, as soon as we let go of the steering wheel, our old programming re-engages. This regression will occur until we reprogram ourselves with new programs, those of our new goals. Our autopilots are always running. The only reason we are not "flying" to our targets is that our desired destinations haven't been programmed in yet.

You are flying to a past preprogrammed destination. If you like your trajectory—the current path you are journeying down—do nothing. If you do not like marching in that direction and you desire a new destination, then it is critical that you modify your programming settings. Our results depend on the programs we install.

Here is a word of caution: It does not matter whether these programs materialize consciously or unconsciously or whether they exist with or without our knowledge. If you possess a program, it possesses you. Remember, the subconscious controls 95% of everything we accomplish. **To create permanent change, we must use the conscious mind to reprogram the subconscious mind.** Simply trying harder will NOT work!

"TRY SOMETHING DIFFERENT" BY PRICE PRITCHETT

Originally entitled "A True Story" from You[2]

I'm sitting in a quiet room at the Millcroft Inn, a peaceful little place hidden back among the pine trees about an hour out of Toronto. It's just past noon, late July, and I'm listening to the desperate sounds of a life-or-death struggle going on a few feet away.

There is a small fly burning out the last of its short life's energies in a futile attempt to fly through the glass of the windowpane. The whining wings tell the poignant story of the fly's strategy—try harder.

But it's not working.

The frenzied effort offers no hope for survival. Ironically, the struggle is part of the trap. It is impossible for the fly to try hard enough to succeed at breaking through the glass. Nevertheless, this little insect has staked its life on reaching its goal through raw effort and determination.

This fly is doomed. It will die there on the windowsill.

Across the room, ten steps away, the door is open. Ten seconds of flying time and this small creature could reach the outside world it seeks. With only a fraction of the effort now being wasted, it could be free of this self-imposed trap. The breakthrough possibility is there. It would be so easy.

Why doesn't the fly try another approach, something dramatically different? How did it get so locked in on the idea that this particular route and determined effort offer the most promise for success? What logic is there in continuing, until death, to seek a breakthrough with more of the same?

No doubt this approach makes sense to the fly. Regrettably, it's an idea that will kill.

Trying harder isn't necessarily the solution to achieving more. It may not offer any real promise for getting what you want out of life. Sometimes, in fact, it's a big part of the problem.

If you stake your hopes for a breakthrough on trying harder than ever, you may kill your chances for success."

You do not have to live out the rest of your life like that fly. Most likely, the ideas in this book are dramatically different from what you have been doing. I am offering you information on how to reset or readjust the autopilot program currently running your life. You might ask, "How do I know what programs are running?" Simply put, look at your results. What is happening in your life? Programs leave clues. Your results are clues left behind by the current programming running your life. If you don't like the results, you must change the program. End of story.

The good news is that once you know how to change the program and apply that knowledge, you can then—and only then—begin to enjoy a new direction and new results. At that time, you can also apply this knowledge to change the programs for any other area of your life you choose to improve.

This realignment works for every area of life. You can enjoy heading in a new direction with much more ease, because the autopilot system won't be fighting against you. Instead, you will work together. During a commercial flight, have you ever noticed the pilot getting out of the cockpit and walking back to use the restroom? You can appreciate that even though the pilot guides the plane, the autopilot flies it. Your conscious mind guides you (your plane) to your destination, and your subconscious mind (your autopilot) flies (controls) you!

Where Did Our Programming Come From?

You might ask, "How did my programs come to be?" That is a great question. Your genetic makeup plays a part, and, in my opinion, your environment plays an even more important role. During your life, you have been exposed to many different people, such as your parents, teachers, family members, and friends. In addition to those individuals, it is likely that you were exposed to other influences, such as television, movies, songs, radio, magazines, and religious teachers. Almost everything in your environment contributed to your programming. In my experience, many, if not most, of our programs steer us off course. Not all of our programs may help us to reach our objectives. In fact, some may propel us in the completely opposite direction.

On the first day of class, Michael Brancheau, one of my college instructors, told us, "Ninety percent of everything we have ever been taught is a bunch of crap." He didn't tell us which 90% was crap. He left that for us to decide. That message stuck with me, and it took over a dozen years before I finally and fully grasped what he said that day.

Most of our behaviors, habits, and paradigms have been passed down from generation to generation, so many things we think and do are based on information from decades, if not centuries, ago. Most of it is old information. We now know so much new information, but it sometimes takes years for it to be incorporated into society.

For instance, after the Wright brothers took the first flight on that historic day in Kitty Hawk, it took "society" about five years to finally believe it had really happened. Our communications systems have improved dramatically since then, so our messages can spread more quickly, but we may not adopt new ideas any faster. To many of us, 90% of what we have been taught may *not* seem like a bunch of "crap," especially because we may have repeated some of that information every day of our lives. That is conditioning. How do you create a belief? Through repetition.

A belief is a thought repeated over and over.

No one is born religious or obese. We were either raised that way or not. What infant is born prejudiced? Babies are not born prejudiced. They pick up those ideas from their environment—that is our conditioning. Remember, **a belief is a thought repeated over and over.** Some of our beliefs have been planted by usually well-meaning people who love us. However, they may have been ignorant regarding certain things. More than likely, they were ignorant about how important a child's mental diet is.

As young children, we usually had to accept our parents' input as fact in order to survive. We listened and, for the most part—if not always—believed whatever they told us. This situation continued until we reached an age when we could think for ourselves. However, even then, we still were not truly thinking for ourselves. For example, take these world-famous characters: Santa Claus, the Easter Bunny, and the Tooth Fairy.

For many years, I enjoyed the fun and excitement of pretending until I reached the age of understanding. Then, I felt betrayed. These ideas and characters were based on a tradition of the people who raised my parents. They were passing on the ideas and conditioning their parents passed on to them. To continue the cycle, my parents passed on to me and to my brothers and sisters many of those same ideas and traditions.

I loved my parents, and they did a great job raising their children. Were they perfect? No, but who is? They did the best they could with what they had to work with at the time, and, most likely, so did your parents. I don't know your parents or how you were raised, but I believe they did the best they could. People can only be or do as good as their programming permits.

I believe that just about everyone is doing the best he or she can, even if it looks as if they are not trying. In that case, "not trying" is the best they can do. Some people might not like their parents. If you fall into that category, remember that they did the best they could with what they had. What our parents did is based mostly on what happened to them in their lifetimes and their environments at the time they grew up. Many of the ideas passed on to our parents and grandparents may have been true at one time, but they are not necessarily true now.

Now, back to Santa Claus. I was told Santa Claus delivered presents to all the good little girls and boys on the planet—and he did it in one night! Children are very bright, but if a lie is repeated by enough people in "authority" enough times, then that lie becomes their truth. It eventually becomes a belief. In the eyes of a young child, adults are trustworthy. Therefore, of course, I believed them. Why wouldn't I? Maybe you did too. As time went on, other kids were let in on the secret by older siblings, friends, or their parents. Depending on when they were told, they may have missed a few years of fun. Eventually, they did discover the truth.

Yes, it was fun and exciting to believe in these famous characters. Enthusiasm and anticipation overflowed every Christmas and Easter, as well as when I lost the occasional tooth. I still remember the day I discovered for myself, with my own eyes, that Santa Claus was a myth. Never in my entire young life had I felt so betrayed and lied to. How could they do that to me? I was truly in shock for a time. We are always supposed to tell the truth, and they had lied. Everyone had lied. It was a conspiracy!

One year, about the time when I began to question this whole concept, I remember watching the nightly news on Christmas Eve, and the anchorman said that the satellites had picked up some activity at the North Pole. This bulletin swayed me to keep believing, because I figured the news people would tell us the truth. Well, we now know better, don't we?

Depending on your parents and your upbringing, you either experienced these characters or you didn't. We're not going to debate here whether being told these stories was right or wrong, as I am drawing out a very important point. These ideas may seem either big or small. Nevertheless, this is exactly what I mean about conditioning. **It may be more difficult to see the conditioning of the "smaller things," but they are there all the same.** In many cases, we don't recognize the smaller ideas and characters, but they are still with us.

Please understand that my entire experience with those childhood traditions was great and I wouldn't change a thing. I was fortunate that I had a blessed childhood with many great experiences. Did I have challenges, too? You bet. The reason for this example is not to complain. It is to illustrate the "programming" that begins at a very young age. These programs were discovered to be erroneous, so we altered our beliefs about them. In many cases, other programs are passed on to the next generation and are not discovered to be erroneous. Then, they continue to run for the remainder of most people's lives. How many other erroneous programs are still running our lives that we don't even know exist?

How many times were you told "You can't do that," "You are too young," "You are too old," or "You are not smart enough"? Some estimates say a teenager has heard the statement "No, you can't!" over fifty thousand times and heard "Yes, you can" only about five thousand times. Remember when we talked earlier about beliefs? **Beliefs are thoughts that are repeated.** Fifty thousand times is a lot of repetition. In my household we do not allow the word "can't."

Besides the fairy tales, there were or are many ideas others told us that may or may not be true. We either believed these ideas or we didn't. As children, we most likely believed them, because they were coming from people of authority. These may not have been true and, most likely, are not true to this day. Because we were children, we didn't know any better and we absorbed that information, regardless of whether it was true. It then became a part of our programming.

You may have been programmed to believe that you are fat, lazy, or always late, that you never pick up after yourself, that you are helpless, mean, or a monster, that you'll never amount to anything, or that you are a loser. These are a few of the infinite possibilities of negative and limiting ideas that could have been programmed into our young minds. The range of ideas—from the lowest negative to the highest positive—is quite large. Depending on our upbringing and our environment at the time, our programming could have been good or terrible or anything in between. As we continue to learn and grow, many of these programs have been unearthed, resolved, and replaced with more empowering programs. However, many have not. What programs are running your life? Are they helping you reach your ideal life, or are some of these old programs holding you back?

Thinking Through Our Own Filters

We do not want to place blame on everyone else. Once we get to a certain age, we begin to decide for ourselves and we commence to "think" for ourselves, although this is based on our previous programming. Everything we take in is filtered by our perceptions, which were created by our programming. Even now, as you read this, you are filtering this information based on your programming. Either you are saying, "Yes, this sounds true" or "No, this isn't true." Those answers are based on your perceptions.

We have all heard of an instance in which a crowd of people witness the same event but each person gives a different account or perspective of what happened. Even though each "saw" the same thing, his or her perception of what really happened may differ significantly from what other witnesses describe.

We know they all saw the same event. However, what others described was different because they were different people. Each person has a different filter. As the event is taken in through the filter, it is distorted. In some cases, it is enough to make others wonder whether that person was describing the same event they saw.

As we read a book or watch a movie for the second or third time, we often see things that we didn't see or read the first time. We may even think they were not there before, yet we understand that, of course, they were there. Why? How did we miss them? We picked up on such details the second time because we were different people than we were on the first go-through. The book or movie didn't change; we did. For this reason, I seriously encourage you to read this book at least three times. I promise you that you will pick up something new each time. This phenomenon happens because you grow with each reading or viewing.

What does all this have to do with reprogramming ourselves to achieve health and fitness goals—or any goal for that matter? We are laying the foundation for you to realize not only the importance of retraining your mind, but that retraining goes beyond being just a good idea. Actually, retraining is essential.

Our success depends on our knowing the following:

- Our programs are still running.
- These programs run our lives.
- Changing our programs is essential.
- We can change our programs.
- Our new programs can create new behaviors.

Some people may wonder if retraining or reprogramming is brainwashing. I have a friend who says, "We need to wash all that garbage out of our minds" [and put in the new, positive, and powerful]. We do need to wash our brain cells, as he puts it. The *New Oxford American Dictionary* defines "brainwash" as "Make someone adopt radically different ideas by using systematic and often forcible pressure." Let's face the truth. We have been gently and subtly brainwashed regarding almost everything we have been brought up to believe.

Our parents, siblings, other family members and friends played a major part in creating our beliefs. They were not the only origins. Other sources have contributed to our adopting certain beliefs. Teachers, ministers, rabbis, or others in positions of perceived authority contributed to our programming. Also, newspapers, television, and radio news stories, advertisements, and TV shows can create certain beliefs. Furthermore, movies and magazines can make an impact. Each has its own agenda.

If you go into just about any grocery store, you'll see on the front covers of a dozen magazines what our society is being brainwashed to believe is acceptable regarding looks, weight, and fashions. These ideas are gently and systematically repeated over and over (repetition creates beliefs) to create a need for us to buy the products shown. Even though we are constantly bombarded with suggestions, ultimately, we are responsible for creating our belief systems. It is—and has been—up to us to accept or reject what we are being told.

According to all those airbrushed photos of models and celebrities, which make them look perfect, we have big shoes to fill. Do you think you have been brainwashed? Brainwashing is going on around us all the time. Quite often, it is neither positive nor empowering. Have you noticed the number of drug commercials on TV? As they approach a trillion-dollar global business, the drug companies are pushing their prescription drugs. Are they brainwashing us to believe we need prescription drugs to be happy and healthy? Isn't that an interesting question? It would be difficult for anyone to dispute the repetition of pharmaceutical commercials. Remember, brainwashing is making someone adopt radically different ideas by using systematic and often forcible pressure.

Everything that has the opportunity to go into your mind on a consistent or repeated basis can have an impact on what you think, feel, and believe—and even what actions you take. This situation has existed for as long as you have been breathing. What do we do about this? This is where the reconditioning process comes in.

Now, you know how important it is to take action on the reconditioning process. As previously discussed, we have programs running and many need to be replaced. Changing some of these programs requires taking certain reprogramming actions.

Remember that there are **two types of actions you must put into play**. The first is action toward your reconditioning process, which we will cover in greater detail in the next section. The second action requires the actual steps to complete a task or deed that must be performed to create a habit. To change your autopilot, you must take action to change the program.

> "Every action has an equal and opposite reaction."
>
> **—Sir Isaac Newton**

The second type of action entails actually doing the actions of the task or habit you intend to implement in your life. In my case, my intention was to exercise every day, so I needed to take action. I had to exercise, which I did. Action is critical for success.

We can take all the reprogramming action in the world, but if we neglect to listen to our nudges (subconscious mind) to go exercise or to eat healthy or whatever the actual implementation act is, we are only taking half the actions required for success.

When I began my reconditioning process, I took action daily on my reprogramming process. Eventually, I heard my inner voice ask me a question as I was writing down my affirmations. As I wrote "I exercise every day," my subconscious mind asked me, "Why don't you go do it?" I thought about it for a few seconds. Then, the next thought that popped into my mind was, "Just do ten minutes." I thought to myself, "I can do ten minutes." It was on that day that I took implementation or achievement action, and I never looked back. Eventually, you must take the actions that will move you toward your objective. In my case, it was exercise. Eventually, I added eating healthier, but it all began with the reprogramming of my mind.

> "As ye sow, so also shall ye reap."
>
> **—Jesus**

TEACHING POINTS

- ☑ There are two main actions to take:
  - reprogramming actions
  - achieving actions
- ☑ You are worthy and we need you.
- ☑ Reprogramming is a process.
- ☑ Appearances are deceiving.
- ☑ Our five senses are limited.
- ☑ We all have earlier programs running.
- ☑ Autopilot lightens the load.
- ☑ Working harder is not the answer; working smarter is.
- ☑ Our programs came from:
  - our genetics
  - our environment

- ☑ We think through a mental filter.

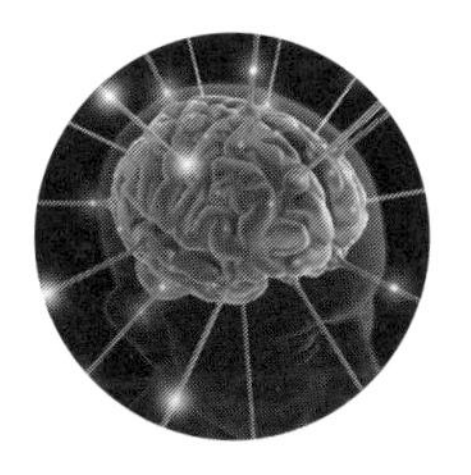

CHAPTER 12

Reconditioning

> "A mind that is stretched by a new experience can never go back to its old dimensions."
>
> —Oliver Wendell Holmes

There are four major areas of reconditioning that have significantly helped me reprogram myself to achieve the level of success I now enjoy. I ask you to keep an open mind as you read on. You may have already heard or read about some of these ideas. Hopefully, how I'm going to describe them will make an impact on your life forever. Here is a word of caution: These ideas may appear simple at first. Therefore, please do not underestimate their power. Use them correctly first, and then you can be the judge.

The four cornerstones of reconditioning are:

- AFFIRMATIONS
- VISUALIZATION
- MEDITATION
- MENTAL MARTIAL ARTS

Years ago, when I first became aware of some of these tools, I had trouble using them. One reason I was unsuccessful implementing these life-altering ideas was that I did not understand how they worked. I doubted that they were a valid solution to my problem, and I needed proof. For that reason, I will discuss the science behind these ideas. We will discuss each technique and the reasons they work when used correctly. I will make these concepts simple to understand. With the latest scientific evidence now present, these ideas become easier to accept, and the more you believe in a method or technique, the more likely you are to use it.

Your success increases dramatically when you understand that the ideas you are implementing are backed with scientific evidence. In fairness to the teachers and authors of my past, much of this research did not exist then. In recent years, we have advanced significantly regarding the understanding of the brain and mind. Today, we possess better technology, which enables us to see and understand more about the brain than ever before.

We truly live in a great and amazing time. For example, we can now watch the manifestations of thoughts in the brain as they happen. This advanced technology has given us greater insights and a new understanding. Along with this new knowledge came the proof that helps inspire us to use these ideas to gain the success we seek. Let's begin.

Affirmations *are repeated positive statements of thoughts or new beliefs that we choose to install or implement into our lives. There are an infinite number of ways to implement affirmations. I have found that affirmations* *work better when performed in a certain way. Here are a few ideas to focus on to elicit the best results. These ideas worked well for me.*

"Empty your cup so that it may be filled; become devoid to gain totality."

—Bruce Lee

AFFIRMATIONS

An affirmation MUST be:

1. a positive statement
2. stated in the present tense
3. written down
4. repeated frequently and consistently
5. used with emotions; power lies in the emotions or feelings
6. backed by action

Following is one of the affirmations I used when I began this process a few years ago:

"I exercise daily, so I'm in excellent shape. I weigh 195 pounds, with body fat of less than 10%. I have a 32-inch waist with rock-hard six-pack abs. I have an abundance of physical and mental energy, and I feel and look great. I am the healthiest I have ever been. I eat healthy foods and drink plenty of water. Being happy and healthy is my highest priority. Every cell in my body vibrates with health, healing, vitality, and love. I am perfectly healthy, and I do all things properly to maintain and improve my health. I think healthy thoughts. Every day, in every way, I am getting better and better. I am healthy, strong, and filled with energy and vitality."

Notice that I didn't say "I will weigh 195 pounds." Instead, I said, "I weigh 195 pounds." My affirmation is stated in the present tense, as if it were already achieved. The subconscious mind does not know the difference between what is real and what is imagined. However, if you are always projecting it into the future, the future is where it will stay.

Actually, the conscious mind needs to be in the present here. When you state your affirmations as if your goal were happening right now, the subconscious mind sees and hears it as happening now. After a period of time, when the reprogramming takes effect, the subconscious mind begins to make your goal a reality. This happens because the new conditioning has established a new comfort zone and now homeostasis is at a higher level. The affirmation is now the new norm and the subconscious mind will strive to fulfill that picture in a number of ways, such as sending suggestions to the conscious mind in the form of thoughts and ideas.

Every time you write, say, read, or hear an affirmation, it is like taking a trip down the new trail through the woods. (Remember my trail blazing story from chapter 3?) Affirmations are important as long as you do them right, and, assuming you follow the instructions laid out earlier, you will be on the right track.

The Science Behind It—the Why

As a quick refresher, **an affirmation must be written down as a positive statement in the present tense and repeated continually.** By "continually," I mean every day or, preferably, one to three times each day. Furthermore, you must add emotion to the affirmation statements and here is the reason:

When you add emotion to the statement (or thought), it releases proteins at the synaptic gaps (the spaces between the brain cells) that create a stronger bond, thus making the connection better and that thought or habit stronger. The more emotion experienced at the time of the thought, the more protein will be released. The stronger the bond, the stronger the neural net. The stronger and faster the neural net is formed, the more quickly the habit is created. The sooner the behavior is changed, the faster the results.

An affirmation must be written down as a positive statement in the present tense and repeated continually.

There are many ways to use affirmations. You can write them down; read them out loud; read them in front of a mirror; and/or record them on a CD, MP3 player, or cell phone. You can listen to affirmations any time, such as while exercising and even when you are sleeping. You can also make a PowerPoint presentation or a slideshow of your affirmations. There will be more about that option in the section on visualization.

You can put your affirmations on index cards or use a program on your computer to flash your affirmations on the screen randomly. Use your imagination. You are limited only by your creativity**. The sole requirement is that you feel good when you are using your affirmations, and the most important aspect of this process is that you feel the emotions.** Whatever you can do to elicit those positive emotions will greatly help you in creating those new beliefs. Thus, you will be creating new behaviors. I have used all of these methods at one time or another, and I still use many of them today.

As you progress, you will alter and tweak your affirmations and your ideal life affirmation sheet, which is a page containing your affirmations. It is a good sign that you are progressing when you are fine-tuning your vision, goals, or the beliefs you want to instill. Bravo! After a period of time (this was several months for me), you'll be satisfied with your ideal life affirmation sheet. When you get it right, you can stick with this sheet every day from then on. All you will need to do is make a few adjustments when you feel prompted to or as you achieve something that you can take off the list.

The most important aspect of this process is that you feel the emotions.

Daily Card

A daily card is a little card you carry with you in your pocket. Every day, before I started my work day, I would write down my top five major intentions. I did this for forty-five to sixty days. One day, about thirty to forty days into my personal reprogramming, as I was writing down one of my affirmations, "I exercise every day," a thought popped into my head: "Why don't you go do it?" The thought was in my voice. Then I asked myself, "Why not?" The next thought came: "Just do ten minutes." Consequently, on November 14, 2006, I went downstairs, began my exercise program, and have not missed a single day since. In the past, the longest I ever stuck with an exercise program was two to three months, at best, and that wasn't every single day either.

Before I knew what was happening, I was on the treadmill and walking to begin day one. I got on the treadmill and exercised for the first time in a mighty long time. Even though the programming of my mindset started thirty to forty days earlier, on that day, I began my new life.

I had programmed my subconscious to *believe* "I exercise every day." Because that was the new autopilot program, my subconscious mind began to execute that program. I unconsciously talked myself into exercising that day, or my subconscious mind talked me into exercising. With a new understanding, using my will, a few strategies we are talking about now, and a big commitment, I was able to do something I had previously only dreamed of. In fact, for twenty years I technically had failed to do it.

Strangely, I didn't even realize what had happened until sometime later, when I reflected back. Then, it was as if I finally realized I was driving a Ferrari when I thought I had been driving a horse and buggy. I realized that if I was able to use these strategies to reprogram this aspect of my life, I could use them to reprogram any area of my life—and I did. I used these same ideas to "brainwash" myself to *believe* that I could write this book, which—at one time—seemed like an insurmountable goal. That, my friend, is what really changed my life forever. An amazing feeling of freedom and a new understanding came to me because, up to that point, it had been just a theory to me. Now I had experienced that freedom, and, when I did, I reached an entirely different level of understanding, and you will too!

For those people who say affirmations don't work, I strongly disagree. Perhaps affirmations didn't work for them at the time, or perhaps they needed to use them in conjunction with the other ideas we are talking about. Remember, I had experimented with some affirmations before and those hadn't work for me then. Most likely, the affirmations failed for others for the same reason they failed for me. We were not using them correctly AND not in conjunction with the other three reprogramming techniques.

Perhaps it was a lack of commitment or action to back them up. Please note that affirmations alone do not work. If you say to yourself one million times, "I exercise every day," and you don't get off your backside to do the work, it will not happen. Remember the thoughts that occurred to me—"Why don't you go do it? Just do 10 minutes"—and then my making a decision to

Affirmations alone do not work unless you back them up with commitment and action and you use them in combination with the other ideas we've discussed and will discuss.

get up and move my feet. I took action. I was prompted by my subconscious mind, and I made a conscious choice. The choice was to take action.

It is pretty easy to carry a gym membership card in your pocket, but just carrying it around doesn't make you fit. You have to get to the gym and do some exercise. The rest is up to you! **Affirmations alone do not work unless you back them up with commitment and action and you use them in combination with the other ideas we've discussed and will discuss.**

One of the best tools I have found useful is recording my affirmations in my own voice. In addition, I enhanced them with some nice positive background music; instrumental is best. I like Mozart or Beethoven. I even used some pop rock and new age music with minimal lyrics. I didn't want the words of the song to muddy the waters. I wanted to hear only my voice, which I trusted, saying the affirmations, mixed with some nice, relaxing, instrumental music. Ideally, you are looking for music with about sixty beats per minute to help you into a more relaxed state, an alpha state.

I began exercising every day with my new understanding of the brain and mind, while I listened through headphones to an audio recording of my affirmations. Simultaneously, I would read out loud my Ideal Life Affirmation Sheet (a full page of affirmations and beliefs that I intended to create as realities). More details on this sheet will be discussed in a few paragraphs.

At first, this activity felt uncomfortable and even a bit weird. However, as time went on, I became more comfortable with the process and it became my new norm. Using affirmations in this manner is an important action that helps ingrain the statements into the subconscious mind—at least in the first sixty to ninety days of your program. After the initial sixty to ninety days, I felt fairly confident that I had transcended through the toughest part of my reprogramming and that I was well equipped with the right mindset, which would move me into even greater success. Affirmations are powerful, and they are even more powerful when spoken out loud. Make sure you speak your affirmations out loud, at least in the beginning.

I recorded my affirmations to a CD, and then I played the CD while I slept at night. The CD player I bought would loop the tracks on the CDs so that it played continuously all night. When I upgraded to an iPod, I set the player to repeat so that it would play my five-minute track of affirmations and then repeat that same track all night long.

It took my wife and me a while to get adjusted to this nocturnal voice in the room with us. It seemed that even though I had the volume so low that only I could barely hear my affirmations, my wife (who appears to have excellent hearing when I don't want her to hear something) could still hear it. Consequently, I used headphones and earbuds for a while, but it was tough to sleep. Eventually, I went back to playing the audio affirmations out loud, and after about two months, I took a break. It was a great tool to throw into the mix. Occasionally, I still use this approach to inundate my subconscious mind.

A special note: one of your affirmations needs to be something along the lines of "I reprogram my mind every day for at least ten minutes."

Auto-Affirmations

I purchased a computer program online that randomly flashed my affirmations on my computer screen, so that while I was working on my computer, I would get another dose of my affirmations. This is a relatively easy setup, and once the initial installation is complete, it is essentially a passive method of inundating your subconscious mind. Every time I turned on my computer, all I had to do was go about my business, and while I worked, positive affirmations would flash randomly on my computer screen. The program is very flexible and allowed me to customize my affirmations and make adjustments to text size, placements, frequency, and duration of the impressions. I paid $30–$40, so it was reasonably priced. Is this something you could add to your reprogramming process?

Ideal Life Affirmation Sheet

An Ideal Life Affirmation Sheet is an 8½" x 11" piece of paper—or any size that fits your needs—that has the five major areas of your life in affirmation form written on one side and your top vision board photos on the other. (These will be explained in another two pages.)

I read my Ideal Life Affirmations Sheet out loud as I walked, and I would read the affirmation statements aloud as I listened to the same words being read by me on an audio recording.

This approach gave it a kind of *stereo* effect. I would see the words, as well as hear and vocalize the statements. This strategy engaged multiple senses. I was seeing, hearing, and feeling the vibration of sound as my vocal cords generated the sound, which stimulated different parts of the brain. I would read this sheet for about five minutes for the front side. This was my routine in the morning or evening, as I worked out. I would also incorporate reading and speaking the affirmations in the car, office, or whenever I had a free moment. I kept a Word file on my mobile phone so that while I waited in the dentist's office or any other place, I could pull out my phone and read the affirmations. In public places, I read them quietly to myself. Can you find certain situations during a regular day when you can implement this idea?

After the initial break-in period, I became easier on myself. Because I was employing so many different methods to install my new program, I didn't feel the need to be hard on myself whenever I missed a day of one or two different methods. However, there were several methods that I used every day, no matter what. If I thought I was low on reprogramming, I would take action and add another item for that day. I allowed myself to be flexible, and I didn't beat myself up. I was committed, and it was rare if I missed any of my daily practices. Let me emphasize an important point: **every day, I did something, and usually multiple strategies, to reprogram my mind.**

VISUALIZATION

One of the next cornerstones in the process of reprogramming the subconscious mind is *visualization*. This is a great and fun way to create new neural networks in the brain and to train yourself for success.

For many of the same reasons that affirmations work, so do visualizations. Each time you visualize, you are establishing and strengthening your neural network of brain cells, which tie each other together to complete a thought. Visualization is not limited to just seeing an image of your goal or an *intention*. Visualization also includes hearing, feeling, smelling, and tasting—any of the senses you can get involved. The word "visualization" is used because we think in pictures. Most people are visual. Regardless of what modality you use prominently, visualization is a great tool. It is vital that you employ as many of your senses as possible when you visualize, and we will soon explore some examples of how to use the *other* senses.

Your brain thinks in pictures. Consider for a moment your house. When you do, a picture of your house pops onto the screen of your mind. Now, think of your car. The image of your house is gone and a picture of your car pops onto the screen of your mind. We *think* in these images.

When you visualize and *see* a picture on the screen of your mind, make that a picture of the object or objective you are intending to create. The more you *see* that picture, the more you will be comfortable having that idea (or picture) in your life. The more comfortable you grow, the more quickly and easily it will become a part of your physical world.

Vision Boards

Another visualization tool is a vision board. I read about the vision board idea years ago. In fact, I created a notebook version of a vision board. Without knowing the science behind it and with my limited commitment at the time, I didn't get the results I was seeking.

Some time later, I was reintroduced to the visualization concepts by the hit documentary film *The Secret* and later by the book. This time, I put them to work and experienced some amazing results. This is my wish for you as well. Because of my new level of understanding and my new level of commitment, the vision board I created this time was significantly more elaborate. It was more detailed, with dozens of photos. Initially, I had one vision board. Then, after I received some coaching, I learned the correct way to create and use vision boards. This time I created four vision boards. Three were things I wanted to be, to do, and to have, and I then developed another board for my accomplishments.

I used bulletin boards that I purchased at an office supply store. You should be able to get them at most major retail stores that have office supply sections. Your vision boards don't have to be fancy. A few sheets of poster board will work, and they are inexpensive. If you want to get fancy, you can spend more. I paid less than $50 for all four of mine. I put them in my office in plain sight, so that when I looked at my computer screen while I was working, I could see them in the background. Those boards are always in front of me when I am working. When I want to focus on them, all I need to do is move my eyes up, and there are my boards.

A belief is a thought repeated over and over.

My vision boards are great reminders. They keep me focused and help me add more emotion to my visualizations. The images I have on them are pictures of things I choose to have in my life for each of the five major areas of my life: spiritual, mental, physical, financial, and relationships. I have them categorized into things I want to be, to do, and to have.

Digital Vision Boards

Vision boards are not limited to cork boards or poster boards on your office wall. I also created digital vision boards on both my cell phone and iPod. At that time, these were two separate devices. Nowadays, video MP3 players come built into mobile phones. (You've got to love technology.) Because technology advances so quickly, when you are ready to make your vision boards, most likely there will be something even more innovative that you can use to incorporate these ideas. Be creative!

Whenever I am waiting for an appointment, or in any situation when I am waiting, I usually pull out my cell phone and flip through my *portable, digital vision boards*. It is a fun way to keep my target in front of me, and my digital vision boards keep me focused and inspired. Because they are on my cell phone, they are easy to carry wherever I go. You can do this too!

It will surprise you when you discover all the small "pieces of time" throughout your day that you can use for the advancement of your goals. When you begin to implement this idea of carrying your portable vision boards with you and pulling them out every time you have a few moments (instead of watching the TV in the waiting room), you will be using your time most efficiently, and you will love that feeling of self-improvement. It is good to look at the photo images, and the most benefit will be derived when you add emotion while looking at them.

Again, the emotion is what releases the proteins at the synaptic gaps of your brain cells, thus making the bonds stronger and the connections more secure. In turn, you are speeding up the process of creating the results you desire. I am repeating this concept here because these ideas work. For every cause, there is an effect. The more you put in, the more you'll get out.

Picking an Ideal Body Photo

If you could have anyone's body, whose would it be? When I picked my first photo, I chose the image of a man with big muscles. After a few days, as I was looking at this image, I thought to myself, "If I look like this guy, I could contend for a bodybuilding competition." That wasn't what I truly wanted to create for my life. Yes, I choose to be trim, and yes, I choose to be lean with *ripped*, six-pack abs, but I was not inspired to be a big muscleman. Maybe you are, and that is fine. It is your life. Choose wisely. Choose what YOU want. In the beginning, it is OK to start with something that moves you toward your ideal target. The point is to get started and find a photo that will inspire you.

When you have your new image of the new you, how does that feel? Next, you need to superimpose your headshot (face) onto that image. I cut an image from a magazine, copied a photo of my head with a smiling face, and reduced the size of my face to fit the size of the body image. I adjusted the image of my face until it was proportional with the image of my new body. Then I cut and pasted my face onto the image and made several copies. At first, I posted them in a few strategic places.

After a week or two, I posted images of my ideal body everywhere. I put them in my office, bedroom, bathroom, exercise room, and car. I carried one in my briefcase and loaded the digital version onto my iPod and cell phone. It is important that you put your face on this image, so you will get used to and be conditioned to see yourself with a great body. Seeing your new, ideal body image conditions you the same as if you were looking into a mirror.

The idea is to become comfortable with that new image. Initially, it is normal for this to *feel uncomfortable*, especially if the photo you chose is a real stretch. As time and exposure increase, you will adapt to this new image. Eventually, you'll accept it, and when you persist in visualizing and *feeling* long enough, you won't need the photo. You'll look in the mirror and you will see the new image live and in person. If you didn't know any better, you might think it is magic. I look in the mirror now and I smile. Sometimes, I laugh because of how simple and how powerful these ideas are for creating an ideal body. It is absolutely amazing. This stuff works!

I am living proof that the system I followed works, and I want you to have what I have—energy, confidence, and a new zest for life. In addition, to live your ideal life, you will gain the confidence to apply these methods to other areas of your life. All of us can live our ideal lives when we take the time to reprogram ourselves to achieve our intentions.

Here is a quick recap:

- Create vision boards for your home and office.
- Create a vision board for your computer.
- Create a portable digital vision board for your mobile phone and/or MP3 player.
- Create a small top ten (or nine) vision board and put it on the rear side of your Ideal Life Sheet (Affirmation Sheet).
- Create a top five vision board for your daily card.
- Keep your new vision in front of you as much as you can and add emotion.
- Create a top photo and place it everywhere.

My Ideal Life Sheet includes goals written in affirmation style on one side and my top nine vision board images on the back. In the beginning, I had my affirmations on the front (five minutes of affirmations when read aloud), including my five areas of life. On the back, I had four minutes of individual affirmations, which were both specific and general statements. After about ninety days, I revised it to a new format. Now, when I complete reading my affirmations on the front, I flip the sheet over to some nice color photos of some of the same things I just affirmed. It is another way to implant the new program.

If you have never done anything like this before, initially these practices may seem uncomfortable and maybe even a bit weird. As you develop some familiarity with the process, you really begin to enjoy it and you become inspired. If your photos don't inspire you, then look for new photos. You can find many in catalogs and magazines as well as at websites such as Google, Flickr, MySpace, and Facebook. If you find images in printed form, you can simply digitize them by scanning them. If you don't have a scanner, simply take them to an office supply store or a copy store, and they can create a digital file that you can use on your computer, mobile phone, or MP3 video player.

As time passes, you will make adjustments to your vision boards, and, of course, you will move your accomplished images to an "accomplished goals" board. The *accomplished* board is where you place all your photos of goals that you have completed. When you do, I guarantee that you will be smiling, because accomplishing a goal produces a wonderful feeling.

Please note that a vision board is not limited to photos. You can use words, statements, quotes, or affirmations. The vision board concept is wide open. You can take it as far as your imagination lets you.

Wait! There is more! I also created a PowerPoint slideshow of my vision board, so that I can flip through both photos and images mixed with affirmations. When I switched to a Macintosh computer, I created an iMovie (a Mac program) of my vision board, similar to my own movie. Whether you are a PC user or a Mac user, there are computer programs that will allow you to use these ideas.

During a seminar event in San Diego, I saw a homemade movie a fellow had created for *his* vision board. It was about ten minutes in length, and, for a self-made movie, it was amazing! It had music, affirmation statements, pictures, images, and actual video. He also used his voice to read the affirmation statements during sections of the movie. I am not sure what he invested on this production, but the results he reaped were tremendous. According to the presenter, this man quadrupled his business and credited it to starting and ending his day watching his customized movie.

Remember, whatever you do, your reprogramming process needs to be fun. If it feels like work, the effectiveness will be reduced. Here is a small caveat: **initially, it may seem like work, until you get into the habit of doing the work.** After the break-in, which usually takes thirty to ninety days, it should be fun. If it is not enjoyable, then adjust and tweak your process until you find something that brings you joy and inspiration. Everyone is different, so my likes may not be similar to your likes. Be flexible and have fun.

A vision board does help facilitate the visualization process. However, some people are more auditory or kinesthetic, which means they may prefer to hear sounds or may prefer to feel or touch. That is perfectly acceptable, and it is a great idea to incorporate as many modes into your visualizations as possible.

If you are mainly an auditory person, you may choose to put more emphasis on audio for your vision board. You can use sounds to describe your intentions. If it is a strong heartbeat you want, get a recording of a strong, healthy heart. For fun relationships, you may make a recording of people conversing and laughing and listen to that as you visualize. If your intention is to exercise at a gym, take a tour and record the sounds in the gym. Record sounds of people using the equipment and other sounds that you may hear in a gym. If you don't want to create the sounds yourself, you can purchase sounds online by doing a search for sounds. You are looking for the sounds that *convey good feelings* to you or that resonate with you. Ideally, they should inspire you.

Perhaps you are more kinesthetic. You may want to create a hands-on vision board. One of my goals is to own an airplane, so I visited a factory that was 1,300 miles from my home. I got a small model of the plane I want, and it is now in my office. On occasion, I will play with this plane and fly it around my office. This may sound silly, but I consider it *commitment*! Would you act like a child if it would help you achieve your goal?

Do whatever you can do to get the *feeling* you would have if you had already accomplished your intention. That feeling is what we are striving for. What would you feel like if you already had that which you crave?

Powerful? Energetic? Empowered? Confident? Inspired? Motivated? How does that feel? That is the feeling you need to add to your visualizations and affirmations. If your desire is to buy a new silk dress in a size 8, then go buy a piece of silk fabric and hold it in your hand, so that you can feel it on your body. If you really want to send a signal to your brain that you are committed and mean business, go buy the dress in the size you want. That is certainly a commitment. Again, use your imagination and have fun with it.

Do whatever you can do to get the feeling you would have if you had already accomplished your intention.

Champion Athletes and Superstar Actors Visualize

Many of our greatest athletes have incorporated some type of visualization into their sport. Jack Nicklaus visualized each golf shot before he swung his golf club. Bruce Jenner used to visualize for two hours before he trained for the day. He did that for four years—every single day. Ultimately, Bruce Jenner won the decathlon gold medal at the 1976 Olympics.

Wayne Gretzky used to visualize where the puck was going to be, and he would skate to that spot. Wayne Gretzky has scored more goals than any professional hockey player in the NHL. Furthermore, before he was a world-famous actor, Jim Carrey wrote himself a check for $10 million for acting services rendered. He would drive to the Hollywood Hills, sit in his car, and visualize himself as a successful actor on the screen of his mind until he firmly believed his vision. Only then would he let himself go home. Since 1996, Jim Carrey has usually earned more than $20 million per film. Do you think he would say visualization is foo-foo?

While I was working my way through high school and college, I was employed at a bowling alley. I bowled a few nights a week on leagues. I bowled in two leagues regularly, and occasionally I'd bowl in other leagues as a substitute. I must admit that it was a fun job.

After a few years of bowling in these adult leagues, I still wasn't at the skill level that I wanted to be. Likewise, my average wasn't as high as I thought it should be, considering that I practiced all the time and I bowled in several leagues a week. The point was, I was getting a lot of physical practice, yet I still wasn't achieving the results I desired. Eventually, I bought a book entitled *The Mental Game* by George Allen. I also read *Success Through a Positive Mental Attitude* by W. Clement Stone and Napoleon Hill and *Think and Grow Rich* by Napoleon Hill. Using the information I gleaned from those books, I began to visualize my average improving.

After a summer break, I experienced some success in visualizing. When friends and family would ask me what average I finished the year with, I would tell them my highest average. You see, in the leagues in which I bowled the fewest games, I carried the highest average. Averages were calculated based on the number of games bowled. For example, if someone bowls three games and has a great night and bowls a 600 series for three games, his average would be 200 for that night.

Over a period of time, if he is a 200 average bowler, he must keep bowling a 600 series or better to keep his average at 200. If he was just "hot" that first night and he only bowled a 500 series the next night, it would bring his average down to 185. See the difference? I bowled in three to five leagues. In two leagues, I bowled regularly every week, while I bowled very little in the other leagues. In a full season of my regular leagues, I would bowl eighty to ninety games.

Thus, I carried several averages. However, in the leagues in which I would occasionally substitute, I might have only bowled twenty-one to thirty games. Therefore, it would have been much easier for me to carry a higher average in the leagues with fewer games, which I did. This also means that the more games bowled in a particular league, the more difficult it is to carry a higher average.

At the end of the season, when people asked, I would tell them my highest average, which was the truth. However, I would be telling them about a league in which I had bowled fewer games. This might have been a league in which I bowled only twenty-one to thirty games. I was telling the truth. I did carry that average, and if, at the time, I had gone to a bowling tournament I would have had to use that higher average (providing I had bowled at least twenty-one games).

The point is, I started this practice of seeing myself with that higher average. When I averaged 150 in my regular leagues, I would carry a higher average of 165 in the leagues in which I substituted. After telling dozens of people (having a big family helped), I began to believe that I had a higher average. I began to think, "I am a 165-average bowler."

In my mind, I replaced (reprogrammed) the lesser average and focused on the higher average, which became my belief. What you believe, you act on. The next fall, when the new season started, I began to carry the average that I had told people all summer long. I was now carrying this higher average in my regular leagues, and in the leagues in which I substituted, my new average would soar even higher.

The point here is not to deceive others, which I wasn't doing, because I actually would have had to use that average if I bowled in tournaments. What I did deceive was my old conditioning. I talked about it, and I believed it. The higher average felt real to me. Although I was doing some simple reprogramming, I didn't even know it, and I got results in relatively short periods of time. The higher average was *true* in my mind. I believed it, so it came to be. How can you use this concept to achieve your dreams?

You may be skeptical and thinking, "Of course you got better, because you have had more experience and you have practiced." Yes, and please note that I had plateaued for several years at the 150 average level with only minimal increases, perhaps two to three pins a year. My progress was minimal until I started to incorporate this practice of *reconditioning* and telling people my highest average. I learned to feel what it was like to be at that level of bowling. This became the norm for me, and at some point, it officially became true.

Having contemplated all that I have shared about my improved bowling, you are probably saying to yourself, "OK. That is nice, but how can this help me?"

It is simple. Cause yourself to believe and see yourself as already at your ideal body weight. Think of your weight as I did with my bowling average, just in reverse. Imagine yourself stepping onto the scale and the number making you smile, not cry. See the new number on the scale. *Feel* how it would feel if you already weighed that amount—your ideal weight. Cut out an image of the number of your ideal weight and tape it over the number on your scale.

Some things to consider with visualizing:

- A vision board helps facilitate your visualizations.
- Get as many of the senses involved as possible (visual, audio, touch, smell, and taste).

- Use visual, auditory, and kinesthetic methods to enhance your visualization experience. (What do you see, hear, and feel?)
- Visualize one or two times every day for five to fifteen minutes. (Technology and your Ideal Life Affirmation Statement make this easy.)

MEDITATION

The third cornerstone of the reconditioning process is *meditation*. There have been many books written about this subject, and I encourage you to investigate this topic further. My intention is to expose you to meditation and give you what I know and have experienced using it. At first glance, you may be a bit apprehensive if meditation is new to you. As you read more, your comfort level is likely to increase. Meditation isn't weird or just trendy. It is an integral part of my achieving success. There are thousands of research studies on the benefits of meditation, and some of the most prestigious people in the medical field, as well as reputable universities, have published studies that indicate meditation has numerous benefits.

There are several types of meditation, and when I began to practice meditation, I used a few different methods, which I will note here. This is by no means a complete list:

- guided meditation
- brain entrainment
- breathing (focusing on your breath)
- transcendental (using a mantra)

There are probably as many methods of meditation as there are people doing them. These four will get you started. A special note here: **meditation is more personal in nature and experience than all the other processes to reprogramming ourselves.** Meditation is a private experience, although I have meditated in a group setting. With exploration, you will discover your favorite method. I encourage you to stick with it until it becomes a habit. Even if you do not see tangible results right away, stay the course. It may take a while, but know that regular meditation provides benefits to you and your body. Those benefits are numerous, and many are health benefits. Following is a list of just some of the benefits meditation provides:

- reduces stress
- increases energy
- lessens sleep requirements
- increases thinking ability
- improves health
- improves mood
- reduces anxiety
- builds self-confidence
- helps with focus and concentration
- increases productivity
- increases serotonin and dopamine levels, which influence mood and behavior, which, in turn, reduces cortisol (the stress hormone)

There are different levels of consciousness or frequencies the brain operates in. In our waking state, we are in what is called ***beta***. At this level of brainwave frequency, we are alert and going about our day. At ***alpha,*** we are relaxed and focused, which allows the creative energies to flow. You could be in an alpha state while taking a shower. Alpha is a good learning state. In ***theta***, we are drowsy and possibly daydreaming. This is the first stage of sleep. At ***delta***, we are in a deep-sleep state. **Meditation takes you from a higher frequency to a lower frequency. In essence, it relaxes you and your conscious mind.** When we meditate we are calming down and connecting to our subconscious mind and the quantum field.

Mental State	Frequency	State of Mind
beta	14 Hz to 50 Hz	alert and awakened state
alpha	8 Hz to 14 Hz	relaxed, creative
theta	4 Hz to 8 Hz	drowsy, first stage of sleep
delta	.05 Hz to 4 Hz	deep sleep

When I first began meditating, I started with a *brain entrainment meditation*. It is a form of deep meditation in which brainwave patterns are altered and both hemispheres of the brain work in harmony. When a person is not meditating, one hemisphere is dominant and it is not working with the other hemisphere of the brain.

I did this meditation every day for thirty to sixty minutes. The time I invested in this activity produced a multitude of benefits. For instance, once I began meditating, I required less sleep. In fact, I found myself sleeping at least two hours less a day, so I actually experienced a net gain of one hour per day. The investment was worth it in the time I gained. Also, this form of meditation was relaxing and relieved stress.

The entrainment meditation was easy and convenient. I simply listened to a CD/MP3 recording with headphones. The binaural beats of the sound "worked" my brain to higher levels of conditioning. The company whose recordings I used has a series of progressively advancing levels. I would listen to one level for about six weeks and then progress to the next level. I did this every day for over two and a half years, and, as if that weren't enough, I also supplemented with some breathing meditations. These meditations, when used in conjunction with the entrainment meditation, would take ten to thirty minutes.

There were days when I would meditate for sixty to ninety minutes. Does that sound like a lot? This is nowhere near what a trained monk can do. They can meditate for six to ten hours a day. I am not a monk, and chances are, neither are you. This may seem like a huge time commitment, and it is. But, to reiterate, I experienced many benefits, so I kept at it. The time commitment you invest is up to you. Remember that what you put in is what you get out. At the minimum, I would recommend you start meditating five to ten minutes per session and then work your way up to fifteen to twenty minutes.

After about two and a half years of entrainment meditation, I decided to add some variety. I switched to a *transcendental meditation with a mantra*. This also helped with the time issues, as my need for sleep seemed to erode back toward my original required time. I sleep less than I used to before I began a meditation practice, but more than when I first began a meditation practice. I continue to meditate as a part of my daily routine, although I have adjusted the time I spend doing so to about ten to thirty minutes each day.

This is a practice you'll want to adjust to meet your personal needs. You may be thinking that there is no way you can fit one hour of meditation into your day, and at first I thought that too. Also, remember that you may require less sleep. The important part is that you begin and it is OK to start small. Fifteen minutes of meditation is better than nothing. Everyone is different and your experience will be your own.

I've had some very interesting occurrences using meditation. I've used it to find lost personal items through a process known as *remote viewing,* and I have had other strange incidents as well. In my opinion, meditation connects you with your Higher Source, which knows everything. Do you want to connect to that energy? Meditation also helps you to reach higher levels of understanding that you may not reach in a regular day at your normal consciousness.

There are many different meditation practices, and no one meditation is more right for you than another. The key is to find and use what resonates with you. You personally may find that you prefer one method over another. I would recommend that you simply start meditating and choose the method that best resonates with you.

The fourth and final cornerstone for the reprogramming process is performing mental martial arts on your ANTs (automatic negative thoughts).

MENTAL MARTIAL ARTS

The last major technique in the reconditioning process is the practice of mental martial arts or the recognition and conversion process of ANTs. These *automatic negative thoughts* are named this because they seemingly happen all by themselves and because they are negative.

This "ANTs" idea came from Dr. Daniel Amen's book *Change Your Brain, Change Your Life*. I was first introduced to this idea and book by John Assaraf, one of my mentors, at a mindset seminar in San Diego. The concept of taking steps to limit a negative thought was not a new idea to me because, years before, I learned that we have the ability to control our thoughts. However, I did not know how to do it. This method solved that mystery for me.

> "If you correct your mind, the rest of your life will fall into place."
>
> **—Lao Tzu**

What I learned, I immediately put into practice and my life evolved almost instantly. An average human has about fifty to sixty thousand thoughts each day, and approximately 80% of those thoughts are the same five to seven thoughts. Therefore, most of the day, we are thinking the same handful of thoughts.

If these are positive, forward-moving thoughts, all is well. If not, we are in desperate need to take control of them to get on the right track. As we continue to think the same thoughts repeatedly, beliefs are formed. It is certainly probable that some of these thoughts are not positive or helpful in moving us toward our goals. In fact, it is more likely that some are negative and are limiting our success in many areas of our lives. What do we do? Eliminate the ANTs!

As a refresher, remember that **our thoughts precede our emotions, which drive our actions. Our actions determine our habits, which precede our character, which determines our destiny. It starts with our thoughts! When we control our thoughts, we can control our destiny.**

When a negative thought enters your mind, the first step is to acknowledge it. If you don't realize you're having a negative thought, you will not be able to eliminate it. **Step one is to acknowledge your negative thoughts**. At first, this may not be easy to accomplish. Most people don't even realize they have negative thoughts. Be aware; watch your words and the words of others. You must notice your negative thoughts as they occur if you are going to be able to alter them. This means you need to pay attention to your thoughts.

After you notice your negative thoughts, the next step is to **appreciate them**. Thank them for serving you, because, up until this point, a thought was serving you in some fashion. At this point, you realize it is no longer serving you (now, you choose more) and you decide to eliminate that and other negative thoughts. Whenever I am eliminating ANTs, I say to myself, "Thank you for serving me in the past; I no longer need you. I now choose *this*." Then, I state what *this* is. *This* is the new thought I am now incorporating.

Twenty-plus years ago, during my early days of exercising, I would be running or lifting weights when the thought would come to me, "I wonder how long I will make it this time?" My question was both a negative statement and a few questions wrapped into one. It implied that I had failed every time up to this point, so what was going to make this time any different?

"How long will I succeed before I fail at exercising regularly and consistently?" This thought would come to me after about a week or two of exercising. It was not a very empowering thought. In fact, it was negative and it insinuated I would soon fall off the wagon and go back to my old habits of not exercising.

If I had been aware of the ANTs recognition and conversion process (I call this mental martial arts), then, more than likely, I could have continued to exercise regularly—or, at the very least, I would have exercised for longer durations. I believe that this technique, in combination with the other reconditioning tools, would have helped me avoid twenty years of *failing* to exercise consistently. If I hadn't learned these tools, I know that I would not be writing this book. *Thank you* to all my teachers out there! In this universe, everything is in perfect order, even when it is in a state of chaos. It took me twenty years to figure out what I am now able to impart to you in a lot less time.

When I began my program—armed with this new knowledge—I used it to my advantage, which I am suggesting you do as well. Whenever a thought entered my mind such as "You don't have to exercise today; you had a great workout yesterday and your body needs the rest," I became aware of the thought and what was happening. Then, I would say to myself, "Thank you for serving me in the past; I no longer need you. I now choose to exercise every day!"

After several bouts, that particular thought would "give up." Actually, I was rewiring my thoughts. I was using the energy of the old thought, and the next time the thought began to *fire*, I would consciously lead my old thought to the new thought—the thought I now chose, the new thought I was installing. As you continue to replace your negative thoughts with new, empowering thoughts, your negative thoughts will dry up, and eventually you'll have more positive thoughts.

If you have ever seen an aikido martial artist being attacked by an opponent who is throwing a punch, you may have noticed that the person receiving the punch will not try to stop the punch. Instead, he will block it by redirecting the punch—using the energy of the attacker against the attacker. Even if a combatant is charging at a full run, our martial artist will step to the side and somehow use that energy against the attacker to flip him over. He may have to use some other means to bring his opponent to the ground.

What the martial artist is doing is to work with the attacker temporarily and then, at the appropriate time, release him and his energy to protect himself. At the same time, our martial artist is able to defeat the attacker by using the energy of the attacker and redirecting it.

When you use this tool, you are using mental martial arts. We acknowledge that we are being attacked by our negative thoughts, we thank and appreciate them—which puts us in a place to use the energy—and then, we redirect. "I now choose this." At that point, the negative thought is temporarily defeated. In the beginning, the opponent negative thought will get back up and try again. However, as long as we persevere, the attacker will eventually see the futility in confrontation and will finally give up and be defeated.

Do not confuse the simplicity of this process with its potential power. This concept has helped me make major changes in my life. Now, when the occasional negative thought enters my mind, I have the equivalent of a *mental black belt* to deal with it. Knowing how to defend myself mentally gave me a great deal of confidence, which is also a strong and powerful ally to help in the process of achieving my goals. Here are some examples of negative thoughts that I encountered:

- "Why try?"
- "You're going to fail again like all the other times before."
- "This is going to be like last time."
- "This is too much work."
- "Exercise is overrated."
- "I'm not strong enough."
- "What makes you think you will succeed this time?"
- "You're not good enough."
- "You do not deserve it."
- "I'm not smart enough."
- "I'm not worthy."

Automatic negative thoughts (ANTs) can be in the first or second person. Listen and pay attention.

By no means are these all of the negative thoughts I experienced, but this list gives you an idea of what to look for. We all have negative thoughts from time to time, and knowing what to do with them is critical to your success. I encounter fewer ANTs these days, and when *you* incorporate this technique into your daily practice, you will have less disempowering thoughts too. You now know how to handle negative thoughts, and the more you use mental martial arts, the fewer negative thoughts you will have.

Another variation of this process is to use the words "next" or "stop." **Step one: acknowledge. Step two: say "stop" or "next."** This method can work. For me, it was like trying to stop a punch instead of using the power and then redirecting it. However, I suggest that you test both techniques and decide for yourself which one you prefer. Again, the great thing about these techniques is that you can use them in any and every area of your life. You are not confined to the exercise and fitness arena. Actually, this book can be more than a book about exercise consistency. You can and will decide how far to take these ideas. How can you use these ideas in other areas of your life?

In this chapter, we talked about the reprogramming process. We began with affirmations, which are goal statements written in a positive tone in the present tense. Then, we discussed visualizations and creating a vision board to help facilitate the visualization process.

To visualize, simply use your imagination to put images—on the screen of your mind—of your succeeding at whatever you are striving for. Your visualizations may be predominately images in your mind, but they can be sounds and textures (touching) or other senses and feelings. The more senses you involve in the visualization process, the better and the faster you create the new beliefs that accelerate your success.

We also discussed meditation and a few different types of meditation, which can help clear your mind, reduce stress, and increase your focus, as well as provide many other benefits that a regular meditation routine can provide. Then, we covered mental martial arts. When you incorporate these four processes on a consistent and daily basis, your life will change drastically. Your friends will notice, and you may wonder how it happened. Although these ideas may seem simple, believe me, they absolutely do work.

Mental martial arts:

1. Recognize and acknowledge your negative thoughts.
2. Appreciate a negative thought; be grateful for the thought and for recognizing it.
3. Replace it with the new, more empowering thought.

The ABC version:

- Acknowledge it.
- Be grateful.
- Convert it to a new thought.

Even though these ideas may sound simple, they are not necessarily easy to do. Effort is required on your part. Actually, reconditioning the mind requires a lot of effort, and what you gain will far outweigh that effort. We are all currently running some programs, which we picked up when we were small children and couldn't think for ourselves. Some of these programs are helping us achieve our goals, while some of them are holding us back. Said in another way, some of our conditioning moves us forward toward our goal, and some of it moves us away from our goal.

Many of these programs are really the source of much of our pain and frustration. The reconditioning process enables us to reset the coordinates of our personal autopilot systems. Normally, when someone tries to create a new habit or change a behavior, he or she attempts to make the change by using physical force instead of adjusting his or her mindset. Using physical force is like using a "manual system" to override the autopilot system, which requires more effort. **What most people don't realize is that when they attempt to override their autopilot manually, it reengages as soon as they let go of the controls. This is the leading reason 95% of all diet and exercise programs fail.**

The reconditioning process consists of a handful of strategies. It comprises affirmations, meditations, visualizations, and mental martial arts. This is a very important part of the book. When these strategies are performed correctly, they make a huge difference in your life. We not only talked about the process of reconditioning; we also covered why it works, so you now possess a greater understanding of the inner workings of the brain. With this understanding, you are more likely to believe that the process works, and thus you are more likely to do the work.

A critical note here: no matter what process, system, or strategy you are using, it will not work as well, if at all, unless you really and truly believe that it *can* work. Unless you are successful in changing your mind regarding the effectiveness of these ideas, your efforts may be futile. Recently, I read an article in *Scientific American Mind* that stated that the placebo effect is greatly increased when the value of or cost of the prescription is higher or if the procedure is perceived to be greater. The power of the mind is truly amazing.

Until you change your old belief system, you are eventually destined to fall back into your old behaviors. Decide, commit, and take action to change any negative beliefs that you may have regarding the reconditioning process.

These ideas have really worked for me, and, if and when you put forth your best effort, they will work for you, too. You can recondition yourself. You can reprogram yourself. Based on the new programs you install, your behavior will follow those settings, and you will do what needs to be done to achieve your objectives.

Of course, having the correct strategies is key. If you do the work outlined so far and you are facing in the wrong direction, you'll be heading in the wrong direction at a faster pace. As you decide and become clear on exactly what your vision is, the Law of Attraction will kick in. (It is always working!) Then, the right strategies and tactics will show up.

To reprogram yourself successfully, the entire time it takes is very important. However, the initial period of this process is critical. Stick with it. Initially, when you choose to change your habits, it requires a lot of focus and willpower, and it even requires more than that. This might sound like a great deal of work, but please stick with it. It is going to require some effort, but I promise that it is worth it. Once you put in the effort up front, it will pay off in huge dividends.

Accomplishing your objective of reprogramming yourself is like getting an airplane off the ground. At first, it takes a heavy throttle (a lot of gas), but once you get some momentum, you can take off. When you get to cruising altitude, you can then ease up on the throttle. Cruising altitude is the place where this book and these ideas can take you, assuming you read, study, and apply what we are talking about. The accountability portion of this process is like the air traffic control tower, which is making sure you are cleared for takeoff so that you can enjoy a smooth ascent and a successful journey. In the next chapter, we will discuss *accountability* and how to incorporate it into your plan.

What most people don't realize is that when they attempt to override their autopilot manually, it reengages as soon as they let go of the controls. This is the leading reason 95% of all diet and exercise programs fail.

TEACHING POINTS

- ☑ There are four main cornerstones to the reprogramming or reconditioning process:
  1. affirmations
  2. visualizations
  3. meditations
  4. mental martial arts
- ☑ Affirmations and visualizations work because they build and reinforce a network of brain cells, which makes the new thought or idea the path of least resistance.
- ☑ Affirmations must be:
  - stated positively
  - stated in present tense
  - written down
  - repeated frequently
  - used with emotion
  - followed by action
- ☑ Visualizations can use any or all of your physical senses.
- ☑ Meditation is slowing down the conscious mind to allow insights, which flow through the subconscious mind.
- ☑ There are numerous types of meditations. Find and use a method that best resonates with you.
- ☑ Fifty to eighty thousand thoughts occur to the average person every day. About 80% of those thoughts are the same five to seven thoughts.
- ☑ Perform mental martial arts on your ANTs (automatic negative thoughts) and convert them into positive thoughts.
- ☑ Mental martial arts = acknowledging, being grateful, and converting ANTs to better thoughts.

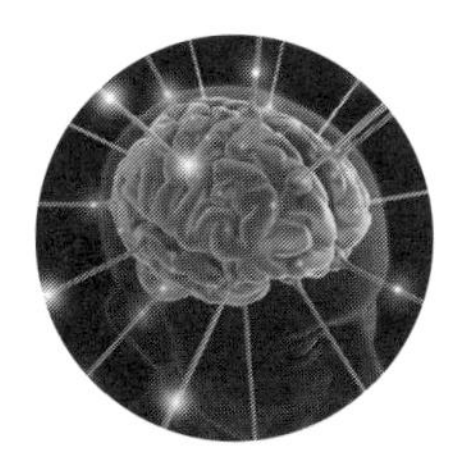

CHAPTER 13

Accountability

"The secret of success is constancy to purpose."

—Benjamin Disraeli

You have now begun a new behavior of reconditioning yourself. Because this is a new behavior that you are implementing into your life, **you will need to make sure you persist in the reconditioning process**, so you can develop the *habit of reconditioning*. A great way to do that is to acquire some help along the way. It is my experience that you must complete the reconditioning process or else you will revert back to your old programs.

Getting help along the way is a wise idea. We do that by controlling our environment and using it to the best of our ability. There are many different environments to which you are exposed, and our main concern at this point is the people you are around.

To help you keep true to your word and use these ideas, I encourage you to add *accountability*—both a personal accountability and an external accountability. **Using the help of others to hold you accountable is critical to your success and will cut years off the process.** Accountability is a great way to keep you on track, and there are several ways to hold yourself accountable. I list some that I have used. You have a wonderful imagination, so open it up and use it as well.

Here are some of the ways I used accountability in the process of reprogramming myself:

- coach/mentor
- friend/buddy
- family: wife, children, parents, siblings
- mastermind group
- daily goal card
- journal
- personal "tracking" calendar

Let's talk about each of these.

Coaches and Mentors

The first accountability ideas we will discuss are external or *public* accountability methods. **In my opinion, the most impactful method of the external approaches is the use of a coach or mentor.** Coaches can come in many different forms. I have benefitted from both a coach and mentor(s). The first time I hired a coach, I bought a block of time, and we spoke once a week for several months via phone. I learned something new from each appointment, and my coach also held me accountable.

Because I knew that I needed accountability and direction, we determined that I would work on an assignment for the week and report back the next week. Then, I completed the assignments my coach gave me, which I may not have done if I were going it alone.

This method worked well for me, and it will for the majority of the people who have a coach. I was able to do things that may have been more difficult to do had I been attempting them by myself. Essentially, what this approach does is shorten the learning curve and accelerate a person's progress.

Furthermore, goal accomplishment comes much sooner with a coach than if you attempt it alone. Obviously, there was a financial investment involved, but the cost not to have a coach would have been more expensive. It makes sense to hire someone who has already invented the wheel, one who can show you how you can make a wheel too. I progressed more easily and quickly as a result of my hiring an expert to help, and I still do this. The benefits of the coaching were so powerful that I have blogged about it, written articles about it, and even mentioned it in my first book I coauthored, *The Power of Mentorship: Finding Your Passion*. I know this topic is very important, so I am mentioning it again in this book. Here is a question for you: why does Tiger Woods have a coach? At the present time, he is considered one of the best professional golfers in the world. Why would he, of all people, need a coach? He chooses to get better, that is why. He also knows that going it alone isn't wise.

One thing you'll notice about *masters* of various fields is that they know there is always room for improvement. Tiger Woods has a coach because he chooses to get better at his game. Tiger knows a coach will help with increasing his skills and providing accountability. A coach can see things the student may not. Many times, the individual may be too close to the situation, while a coach can see with an outsider's perspective. A good coach can see the pupil's blind spots, and the coach's intention is to help. My suggestion is that if you don't already have a coach, get one, and be sure he or she is a good coach.

As a plug for my business, you may consider working with me. To find out if we have any availability to take on new "participants," send an e-mail to **info@donstaley.com.** If we are booked solid, we can put you on a waiting list, or if you prefer, we can find or refer you to another qualified coach.

Friend or Buddy

If you are presently unable to swing the finances for an expert coach, solicit the help of a friend or buddy. Such a person may not be able to shorten the learning curve, but he or she may provide you with some accountability. Unfortunately, the difference in progress can be significant when you drop down from a professional coach to a friend or buddy. However, something is better than nothing.

When using a friend, do not seek advice unless this person is a professional or has obtained and sustained the results you seek. Otherwise, ask only for him or her to hold you accountable. Examples of how your friend can help are by asking you if you have a certain task completed by a certain date or asking you if you exercised today.

If you ask people who are not professionals for advice and they point you down the wrong road, it may take you longer than if you didn't have a friend or buddy helping you at all. The same situation applies when you are working with a coach. Please make sure that the coach you hire *has been there and done that*. This attention to detail will save you time and money. Just because a coach is certified or has a bunch of abbreviations after his or her name doesn't guarantee that he or she has overcome similar challenges that you intend to conquer.

When asking for advice, make sure that you are seeking it from a professional. If you needed a root canal, you wouldn't ask a plumber to do it. If you had a stopped-up pipe, you wouldn't ask your dentist for help. As long as you pick your friend wisely, you will have someone in your corner who can give you a boost when you need it. The obvious choice is a professional coach, but if you can do both, then hire a coach and recruit a friend to help.

If you think you are not able to afford a coach, you may want to reconsider your priorities. Years ago, I wanted to develop my speaking skills, and a mentor suggested that I take the Dale Carnegie Course. At the time, I was paying my way through college by working two jobs, and I wanted to take this course because I knew that I really needed it to take me to the next level. However, as a college student, funds were tight. I was living paycheck to paycheck and I believed that I just couldn't afford the $900 for the twelve-week course. I told the sales guy, Carl Miller, that I couldn't afford it, and Carl replied, "Don, this is exactly why ***you cannot afford NOT to take this course***."

Ultimately, we worked out a payment plan, and I took the course. It was a big stretch for me to jump before the net appeared, however, at the time, it was the best decision I could have made. As a result of the course, not only did my speaking skills improve, but so did most areas of my life. Everything affects everything else.

Family

You can also get your family involved. However, you may need to be very selective here. Consider your relationships within your family, because you will want to select a family member who loves you and who will support you in your endeavors. This needs to be someone who will be a cheerleader and also will hold you accountable for your commitments.

If you are not able to find a friend or family member who will do it willingly, perhaps you can offer to pay someone to keep you on track.

Relatives can be important to your goal when you get down to details. In our house, we have chosen to eliminate certain nonproductive words from our vocabulary. The excluded words are fear-based and do more to move us away from success than they do to move us toward success.

Examples:

Disempowering Words	Empowering Replacement Words or Phrases
can't (cannot)	still in the process, finding a solution
try	I will do my best, nice effort
need	desire, prefer
want	I choose, my vision is
should, would, could	next time I plan to, from now on
It's just me	It is me, I am here
don't	do
but	and
always	frequently
never	rarely
I'm not	I am
stupid	ignorant

In this book, I have used a few of these disempowering words intentionally as infrequently as possible and only when I thought one was necessary for the sake of clarity.

In my opinion, these words do more to hurt us than help us, so I prefer that we use other, more productive words in our home. I am well aware that we live in a society predominantly driven by negative words and news, and I also realize that for every positive there is a negative and vice versa. The universe is always in balance. If you slice a magnet in half while hoping to get two positives, you will be disappointed. There will always be a positive pole and a negative pole. **The words we choose to use are powerful and can help or hinder us in our progress.**

Occasionally, when my guard is down and one of those disempowering words slips out, my family catches me and I pay one dollar to each person who corrects me.

Our son Nicholas was almost five years old when I began writing this book, and he had already been collecting dollars for nearly two years prior. He may be a child, but do not let his age fool you. Kids are smart and very perceptive. He not only does a great job of keeping my wife and me on our toes, but he keeps watch on the extended family as well. Most of them now know about this little game too. Nicholas may not get rich this way, but it is fun for him, and he gets excited occasionally, when he does collect. For me, it is well worth the money to keep me on track. This game works both ways, as I also keep my family accountable for their words, and we also teach our son a great lesson in the process. **The words we all use are critical!**

You can use a variation of this strategy with your accountability person. Have him or her ask you if you have exercised today—or whatever your goal is. If you have people in your life who, at any time, can ask you, "Did you do 'X' today?" the more likely you will do it. If you are not honestly able to say yes, it will hit your wallet. If it starts costing money when you neglect to take action, you will be more likely to take the action. Use your imagination. You can tweak this idea to fit your situation.

If you have chosen to exercise regularly and you tell your helper—whether this is a friend, family member, or coworker—you *will* set it up so it works with your schedule. If you prefer to exercise in the evening, and early one morning a coworker comes to you and asks if you exercised today, of course you will say no, because you exercise in the evenings. Simply adjust the question. Instead, your helper could ask you, "Did you exercise last night?" or "Did you exercise every day this week?" You should make it work for your situation. Your friend will get a benefit out of it too, either in the form of money or knowing that he or she is helping you. Perhaps you may even inspire your helper to get fit as well. Most importantly, have fun with the process.

Mastermind Group

In my second book, *The Power of Mentorship and The Mastermind Group*, which I coauthored with Zig Ziglar, Brian Tracy, Bob Proctor, and many others, I wrote about my first mastermind group experience. Since then, I have been in many mastermind groups, and they were all beneficial.

A mastermind group is a group of like-minded individuals who are working toward a common goal. Napoleon Hill spent a great deal of space in his famous book *Think and Grow Rich* talking about *accountability* in the form of the *mastermind alliance*. In fact, the *mastermind principle* is one of the sixteen commonalities he found in the top five hundred most successful people of his day. **Simply put, you need accountability—both internal (of yourself) and external (outside of yourself).** Having the right people in place will guide you through the challenges, especially in the early stages of this process.

Shortly after I began the reconditioning process, I got involved in a mastermind group during a weekend business seminar held by OneCoach, a company that coaches small businesses. It was a three-day event, and we were encouraged to connect with people to form a mastermind group.

One of the main reasons for such a group is *accountability*. **Each person is to hold other members accountable for their actions, and when one person is down, the others are there for encouragement.** Many of the attendees got together in different groups—all ranging in size from four to eight people. The group I joined began with five people. Because it was a small business seminar, we were all small business owners, and we were all from different parts of the country.

Even though the members of our new group were strangers to each other, we all had many things in common. We were all there to grow, learn, and take our businesses to the next level. We started with introductions, and each of us told the group some personal things as well as some business background information. We spent about one and a half to two hours that night getting to know one another and telling stories. This was a good group, and we were off and running. In the passion of the moment, we all agreed to a weekly call and a daily e-mail to keep each other on track.

We agreed to rotate the call leadership, with each of us taking a turn at facilitating the call. After we went back to the "real world," we lost one of our members. She seemed committed and excited at the time, but either we were not the group for her or she wasn't ready and committed for our mastermind group. When you get involved with a mastermind group, you may encounter this situation too. It is perfectly OK; we wished her well and kept moving forward.

A few months later, there was another conference, and we picked up two more members. Our group was evolving. This is normal also. After some time, we lost another member and then another. A few months later, at another conference, we recruited a new member. The group changed, but we maintained our two core members—I was one of the two remaining core members. The other one is my new friend Carletus. We did our best to keep the group going and did so for over a year. Even though that mastermind group is no longer together, we all parted as friends. In fact, I still keep in contact with some of the former group members from time to time. Since that group disbanded, I have been involved with several other groups, and, most likely, I will be a part of some type of mastermind group for the rest of my life.

Here is an important key: **a mastermind group may not be a lifetime entity.** It could be. It is possible. It may turn out to last for only a month or two. That is OK. What is important is it will have helped you and your friends grow and move to the next level. The longer the group is intact, the greater the likelihood that each member will benefit. However, just because a group doesn't last forever doesn't mean it wasn't successful. If a group doesn't last long, some people may say the group failed. Maybe it wasn't an absolute success, but there are always many lessons to learn when a student is looking.

Some lessons could be to learn more about commitment, accountability, persistence, giving, caring, showing compassion, leadership, and human nature. This kind of experiential learning is many times more powerful than just hearing or reading about it. Imagine a mastermind group discussion regarding everyone's level of fitness!

Being part of a mastermind group is a great experience, and I highly recommend it. That is why, in the last chapter, there are many assignments to apply and experience after you have read this book. If you acquire nothing else than the friendships that develop from a mastermind group, you will have gained a lot. If you are not a member of a mastermind group, please do consider it as a part of your accountability strategy.

One of the biggest benefits of the mastermind group is the accountability. While being a part of a mastermind group, I know that if I say I am going to do something by the end of the week, then, during the next call or meeting, several others are going to say, "Show me the money," or ask me, "What did you do this week?" It was and is a great tool to use to spur myself on at times when, perhaps, my mood would prefer that I do something else.

Being in a mastermind group is like being on a team. If you have ever been involved in a team sport, you know what I'm talking about. A good team inspires you to do the things that need to get done, even if sometimes you don't want to do them. There may be times when you don't want to do "it" for yourself, but you will do it for the team. When you are on a good team, everyone benefits, as long as everyone is inspired to do, be, or have more than he or she was previously experiencing. A good team member will push everyone on the team, including the leader. **A mastermind group is a team working together to help one another accomplish their goals.**

Taking this discussion one step further, *personal accountability* is another very important part of the accountability process. There are a number of ways you can accomplish this. The three main tools I used for this strategy were a daily card, a journal, and a wall calendar.

The Daily Card Is Also Used for Affirmations

I now carry a daily card in my pocket every single day. I carried such a card every day in the beginning of my reconditioning, and it worked very well, but after a while, I got away from carrying the daily card. It was a new program which wasn't fully installed as a solid habit. Unfortunately, I failed to carry and use it for the recommended 90-120 days. When I noticed many goals were taking longer than what I had calculated them to take, I evaluated the situation and realized the power of the daily card. Therefore, I brought it back into my daily routine, and then my results began improving immediately.

I place value on both the accountability and carrying this simple card in my pocket. For a free sample of this card, visit www.donstaley.com/fitmindbook. This is a link, so when you sign in you can download or view the PDF version of this card as a guide.

Your daily card doesn't have to be complicated. It can be a simple card with your intentions on one side and a general affirmation or quote on the other. Using such a simple card is how I got started, and it has evolved as I have evolved. I would like you to consider starting with a basic card and adding to it as you progress through the process. Here is what I recommend:

- mini vision board
- affirmations
- a positive quote from a famous person or a general affirmation

I currently carry my card with me every day—Saturdays and Sundays too! My daily card has several functions. Mainly, it is to keep me focused on what I choose for my life, keep me on the right track to get there, and remind me whether I did what I needed to do that day.

When the card is updated, which is usually the first thing in the morning, I place it in a plastic sleeve. If I am leaving the office, I put it in my back pocket. If I am working at my desk, I leave it out so I can see it. I carry this card wherever I go 24/7/365. The only exception is if I am swimming, showering, or doing another activity where it could get ruined. In those cases, it is nearby, and when I finish with that activity, the card is with me again. At night, after I review the day and move any unfinished business to tomorrow's list, I put the card on my nightstand, so I will see it first thing in the morning. Accordingly, as I get out of bed in the morning, it is the first thing I reach for.

Using this card is a tremendous help in the reconditioning process, and I truly doubt that I would have written this book if I hadn't employed the ideas that coincide with this card. I highly encourage you to use the card idea from the beginning of your reprogramming strategy.

The greatest advantage about this card is that you can carry it anywhere. This card may seem simple, and many of these ideas *are* simple. However, many simple ideas have great potential power. When you develop the habit of using this card, you will be amazed at the rewards awaiting you!

At first, carrying and using your card is a new habit to be formed and programmed into your mind. It may take some time to develop this habit. Learn from my early mistake of discounting the power of this card. I neglected to nurture my new habit for 120 days. When I let one day pass without using the card, it soon turned into two days, a week, a month, and then two months.

As with a garden, if you neglect it, the weeds will take over. Consequently, I have learned that each new little habit seed requires a lot of love and attention, and—above all—it requires time. Be patient. Remember that major changes don't happen overnight. When you condition yourself to do the small and sometimes simple tasks every day for the designated duration, you will eventually see monumental changes.

I must emphasize that **you need to be patient.** This is not a microwave oven. We are slow-cooking here, and the resulting taste will be so much better. In fact, I encourage you to get rid of your microwave! Remove that "I've got to have it now" mentality! Also, there are health benefits by avoiding use of a microwave. Things worth having require time and planning, not zapping. When you get rid of the microwave, you'll need to do a little more planning, and spending a little more time will be worth it. Your food becomes healthier.

When you microwave food, it alters its molecular structure, and it is not healthy. Neither is trying to rush your goals to completion. When you do that, chances are you will get frustrated and disappointed and may not stick with the process. Valuable things take time to develop. **There is an incubation period for everything.** Remember the Law of Gestation?

You might be thinking, "OK, he has done it now! Don has gone off the deep end! Get rid of my microwave? Are you serious?" YES! This is a paradigm shift! The microwave is a symbol of impatience. **To live your ideal life with your ideal body requires you to remain focused and have patience. Eliminate your microwave mentality.**

As I mentioned, I carry my card in a plastic sleeve similar to a name badge holder you get at a seminar or conference. It protects the card and adds some rigidity. The clear sleeve also adds to the feeling you get when you touch the card. When you touch the card and sleeve, it automatically sends a signal to the brain about your goals and daily tasks. The card is one more way to reinforce the neural network of brain cells you are now choosing to create.

Carry the card wherever you go and read it often. When you take it out, you can look at the daily tasks and also have special times to think about the mini vision board and the affirmations. Read your affirmation statements and visualize how you intend your life to be. As you read and visualize, add feelings and emotions. The words are great and pictures are helpful. However, the feelings are the most important factor.

We know that it takes time and repetition to program this process or habit into your daily routine, but as you do it every day, it will get easier. At first, it may seem as though you are taking a machete to cut a new trail. Frankly, you truly are cutting a new trail. Unless you have created this habit already, this is a new experience and will require some effort to get it off the ground—at least initially. Hack away at it for thirty, ninety, or even 120 days. Then after that time, the habit will take over and you will no longer have to exert as much effort.

Wall Calendar

I kept a wall calendar and, each day, I would mark off what tasks I had accomplished for that day. At some point, I reviewed my day—which is another habit I incorporated since I learned how to recondition myself—and I would notice whether I had done my task. Some days were crazy busy, and sometimes my task might get overlooked. One night, I was reviewing my busy day at about 11 p.m. when I realized that I had not completed my exercise for the day. I dropped everything and did my task; I exercised.

Having this wall calendar was a great help, especially before a new habit became ingrained. It is good to have a safety mechanism to protect you on those days when perhaps your mind is distracted by the chaos of the day. It has helped me. If you have this safety net in place and you do forget, you will be grateful it was there to remind you.

You can use a simple calendar, or you can get a laminated calendar that you can write on with dry-erase markers. It doesn't matter which you use as long as you put it in a place where you will see it at the beginning and end of your day. I got a big calendar, which measured two feet by three feet, so it was *in my face*.

Journal

The last major tool I use to hold myself accountable is my journal. I still use it daily to "track" my successes, challenges, and thoughts. I also use it to finish the day with some affirmations. Furthermore, I list the items that occurred each day for which I am grateful. It is a good way to reflect at the end of the day and focuses me on what went well. What we are doing when we are reflecting and being grateful is connecting to source energy, the universe, God, or whatever label you want to use.

One of the great things about keeping a journal is that it only takes a minute to jot down a thought or idea, but as long as you keep the journal, you always have access to what you have written. You can refer to your writings to see how you have progressed. I look at mine and see what I used to value and what I now value, and I can track my growth and development. My personal evolution is easy to witness by reflecting back on my old journals.

My "wanting" for *me* has now become a lower priority than my "wanting" for others. This was a huge shift for me, and it might have gone unnoticed if I hadn't written my daily goals in my journal. I might have missed some inspiration that kept me moving forward, but because of the journal, I was able to recognize my progress, which was inspiring me to keep striving.

A journal is also great for collecting ideas. Daily, you are receiving a boatload of new thoughts, any of which could be a million-dollar idea when implemented. Even of greater value, it could be an inspiration that revolutionizes your health. If you don't capture that idea, it may be gone forever. It is also wise to carry a journal or a voice recorder so that when an idea pops into your mind, you have a way of capturing it. Our short-term memories are only short term. Usually, they can hold information for thirteen seconds to three minutes.

The time to capture a new inspiration is short lived, so devise a method to capture ideas and secure them quickly. If you're in a place where you can write an idea down, write it down. If not, perhaps you can use a voice recorder and then transfer it to your journal later that day. You will be glad you did.

As far as the accountability part of the journal goes, at the end of the day, it is helpful to write down what you have done that day for your top goals. This activity is to make sure that you are doing something to move yourself forward each and every day. When you complete your day, you can evaluate your progress and see what actions you did take. However, it is important to avoid belittling yourself if you miss the mark. Criticizing yourself is not going to help you move toward your goal.

The journal helps you have a better understanding of what you are doing and what actions you are taking. When you look at your daily actions, you can determine, based on these behaviors, what "programs" are running in the background. Remember, 95% of our actions are on autopilot, and our acts reveal our programming. The majority of what we do is being run by our autopilot system, known as our subconscious mind. If we don't like what we see by looking at our daily actions, which are recorded in our journal, we may need to focus more on a particular area or habit to "reprogram" it.

At the beginning of this book, I commented that many of these ideas are simple. However, they may seem tough to implement at times, and when you put these ideas together, they compound themselves and the results are magnified. There are many ways to keep yourself accountable. See the following chart.

External (Others) Accountability	Personal (Self) Accountability
mastermind group(s)	daily card
coach	calendar
mentor	journal
friend	
family	

All of these ideas have helped me in my efforts to create new, empowering habits, and you can use these ideas to improve your life. When you strive with your whole heart, you can change your life. By no means are these ideas the only methods to get you from where you are now to where you choose to go. You have a magnificent imagination when you use it. Put it to use and see what else you can come up with that resonates with you. *When you find a good idea and are willing to share, please send me an email and I will pass it on.* You can make this process fun. If you're not having fun, it will be more difficult to make a shift. Initially, you will want every advantage you can get, not over others, but over your old self.

> "As a man thinketh in his heart, so is he."
>
> **—Proverbs 23:7**

Accountability helps keep you in line and on target toward your goals, it adds more people to your team, and it increases your power and strength—which is stronger than you think. Accountability helps keep you focused, and without some type of accountability, the path to your goal will be a long and lonely road. One of my mentors used to say frequently, "You have to do the work yourself, but you don't have to go it alone." There will be challenging times ahead, and when you have a mastermind group, coach or mentor, or a friend to turn to for support, it will help ease you through those tough times. Plus, there is an "I'll do it for the team" effect related to inspiration. By putting as much accountability into your team as you can, you will enjoy success sooner and have more people to share your success with when you finally accomplish your heart's desire.

TEACHING POINTS

- ☑ Accountability helps to keep you true to your commitments.
- ☑ Use both external and personal accountability.

  external—> coach(es), mentors, family, friends, and mastermind group(s)

  personal—> daily card, journal, and calendar

- ☑ A coach or mentor lends you expertise from his or her experiences and can see your blind spots, thus accelerating your success.

- ☑ Mastermind groups harness the power of the group to help each individual.
- ☑ Beware of unproductive words and use accountability to keep on track.
- ☑ Even a four-year-old can hold you accountable.
- ☑ Use the tools—daily card, journal, and calendar—to track your progress and hold yourself accountable.

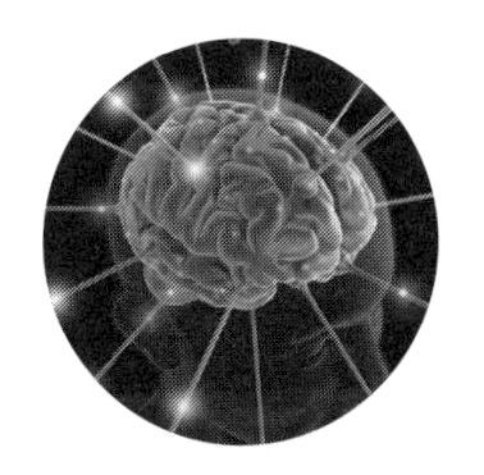

CHAPTER 14

Gratitude

> "But the value of gratitude does not consist solely in getting you more blessings in the future. Without gratitude you cannot long keep from dissatisfied thought regarding things as they are."
>
> 
>
> **—Wallace Wattles**

As kids, we may have been taught to "count our blessings." If you were fortunate, you heard it many times. Being grateful, in my opinion, is a good program to have *installed* in your subconscious and a great state to be in. Have you heard the statement "The more you give, the more you receive"? It is true. It has also been stated, "As you sow, so also shall you reap."

In my life, this concept has been proved again and again. When we talk about gratitude, we are talking about connecting with the source, universe, or God. Remember, it doesn't matter what label we use. **When you're in**

a state of gratitude, you are giving away love. When you give away love, you receive more of it.

If you have a full glass of water, can you receive more? No, not in your present container, unless you drink some, spill some, or give some away. When you pour it out, you now have more room to receive. Similarly, when you give away, you are now ready to receive more. When you are grateful for what you already have, you'll receive more.

Be Grateful for Your Efforts and Results

Let's consider this idea of gratitude on a few different levels. I invite you to incorporate gratitude during your efforts toward your goals. You will notice that you are making progress, and this is a perfect time to be grateful. The more you feel grateful for your advancements, the more you evolve. The more you appreciate your own efforts and progress, the more successes occur. When you can be grateful for your challenges, you have "arrived" somewhat—although we never fully arrive.

You may be thinking, "Why on earth would I ever want to be grateful for my challenges?" ANSWER: So you can be given more!

"Why would I want more challenges?"

The more challenges you are faced with, the more you will overcome and the more you will grow. Yes, be grateful for your challenges. Many people have the wrong idea about challenges and failure, and the reason may be that we were taught that challenges—some people refer to them as problems—are bad. They are not. **Challenges are good. They actually help us learn and grow, so we can move on to the next level.** I challenge you to find someone who is presently experiencing success but hasn't experienced some challenges. In my experience, the bigger the success someone experiences, the bigger the challenges he or she had to overcome.

If you are strong enough to do resistance exercise by lifting fifty pounds, you wouldn't want to lift a five-pound weight. That would be futile! I am not talking about warming up. I *am* discussing the actual exercise using resistance. **We need resistance to get stronger—and not just in the gym**—so we use weights that provide us with a challenge. If this is a new concept for you, be grateful for your challenges.

When I started practicing gratitude for my challenges, it felt weird. It was a strange sensation, not because it was new to me, but because it seemed opposite to what I was used to doing and feeling. Then, as I was able to be grateful for my challenges, I put these personal tests in a new light. A challenge was no longer as big or insurmountable. In fact, each seemed to be a part of my "team." Imagine that! Think of putting all your challenges on your "team." Wow! Now, everyone is on your side, and it is hard to lose when everyone is on your side. **If everyone is on our team, we have no opponent. We win!**

Sometimes, I need to be reminded to be grateful for my challenges. Yes, of course, I too need to be prompted. As I have "handled" and then appreciated my challenges, they melted like a chocolate bunny on a hot spring day. Challenges are like increasing the exercise weights. If you previously got a good workout by using fifty pounds and now you are using fifty-five pounds, you have upped the weight or resistance and you are becoming stronger. *Correspondingly, once you allow yourself to welcome challenges, handling them will also make you stronger.*

If you have not yet seen the movie *The Secret*, I highly encourage you to view it. It is a great documentary on personal growth—specifically on the Law of Attraction. The movie talks about gratitude as a major part in creating what you choose in your life.

While implementing the reconditioning process, here are a few major ideas to use gratitude:

- Be grateful for your efforts.
- Be grateful for your progress (results).
- Be grateful for your challenges.
- Be grateful for your life (past, present, and future).

I invite you to consider using these ideas for the rest of your life.

You Must Be Grateful for Your Current State Before It Improves

When you take the time to be grateful, you're sending out the signal that everything is plentiful, and what you send out comes back. The more you send out, the more that comes back. No matter our present situation, there are many things we can be grateful for. All you need to do is to look for them. The more you practice, the better you get. *Practice being grateful on a regular basis. With time and dedication, you will develop it into a habit.*

Here is another great habit that can completely change the way you look at things and thus change your life: Another one of my mentors, Dr. Wayne Dyer, says, "If you change the way you look at something, the thing you look at changes." Additionally, when you are "looking" at what you *don't* have, it is harder to see what you *do* have. I suggest that no matter how bad it may seem to be in your situation right now, there is something good there at the same time. This has to be true. It is called the Law of Polarity.

As you may remember, the Law of Polarity states that there cannot be a negative without a positive. Also, you may note that the reverse is also true. No matter how good and positive something may seem, there is always a bad or negative. They are both there. According to the Law of Relativity, nothing is good or bad, big or small until compared to something else.

Therefore, neither exists *until you decide* it is one way or the other. Gratitude is critical because what you focus on grows, and what you give your attention to, you love. What you love expands. What do you choose to focus on?

When you place your attention on what you are striving for, that becomes your focus—the good stuff. These are things you truly want to bring more of into your life. When this concept becomes clear to you, your whole life will shift. If you are unable to be happy with where you are presently, whether it is your state of finances or fitness, you will not be happy in your ideal financial situation or your ideal body either. Here is the irony: **when you become happy and grateful for what you have now—and that could be a financial mess or an unhealthy, dilapidated body—then, and only then, will you start to move in the right direction.** Be grateful and happy now, in this moment. Then you will move toward your ideal body and your ideal life.

Be Grateful During the Journey

What is even more amazing is that *being grateful inspires you*, so everything you do about working toward your target seems easier. It no longer seems like work. It becomes more fun! How would you like to have fun most of the time? Yes, I would too! When I started this process of personal growth, I began to have more fun, and the process became easier as well.

When you are *working* toward your intentions and you are having fun, this is when you're in the flow. You are in the current of life, going with the river. When we are in the process, this is where we will have the most fun and where we will grow. **Most people think that it is the destination that brings us the most joy. When you realize that the trip or the journey is where you have the most fun in life, it is then that you add more joy**

to your life. We spend more than ninety-nine percent of our time en route to our destinations until we accomplish them (arrive), and then we set new destinations. Therefore, we are always en route.

Not long ago, a group of my family and friends got into a small bus and rode ten hours to West Virginia to go on a whitewater rafting trip.

When we began planning this trip, we thought that we might take two vehicles and convoy. We then looked into the possibility of taking one vehicle, which would allow us all to ride together. We looked for the perfect vehicle, which met the group's criteria of size, price, and comfort. For weeks, we were unable to locate such a vehicle. We looked at motor homes, vans, and even small buses, but nothing seemed to work. Therefore, about a week before our trip, we tentatively agreed that we needed to take three cars because two would have made things too cramped.

I continued to think that it would be much more fun traveling all together in one vehicle. I held that intention the entire time, but it seemed as if we would be riding in three cars. Unfortunately, taking three cars would require at least three drivers for ten to twelve hours each way. It would require our efforts to be multiplied, and it would have allowed less interaction with one another all the way to the river and back.

Within three days of the departure date, I saw the perfect vehicle. It was a small, private "not for hire" bus. At that moment I decided that I wanted a bus and that we would have one! I didn't know exactly how we would get it, but I was grateful for a "sign," having seen one. It wasn't long before a thought popped into my head to call a company that someone had mentioned weeks earlier, which we had previously checked on and eliminated as a possible option.

When I checked this time, they had a fifteen-passenger bus available with air conditioning, reclining seats, CD player, a television with a DVD player, and plenty of storage space. Because of the timing, they were now more flexible with their rates, and I was able to negotiate favorable terms. Thus, we had a win-win opportunity for all involved. Within a few hours of making this decision, I had secured a small, fun bus, which would allow the entire group to fit into one vehicle and would also reduce our expenses.

There are a few points to this story. One is the power of keeping your intention and being persistent. Two is the power of decision. Three, there are usually several ways to travel to your destination, and even though each method will get you there, one method may be more fun than the others. I suggest picking the option loaded with fun! Either way, be grateful for the journey.

Six of us took turns driving one to three hours. We rode in style, playing music and movies and enjoying the trip in comfortable, reclining seats with plenty of leg room, lots of storage area, and open spaces. Most important, we got to visit and interact with each other all the way there and all the way back. The ride was almost as much fun as whitewater rafting itself. You can also think of the group on the bus as our accountability team, all striving toward the same objective and all celebrating when we reached our destination.

The main point of the story is that we are always on a journey, so why not enjoy it? In life, we may not always be on a bus with all of our friends, but we are on a journey nonetheless. It is **our decision to be grateful** for as many aspects as possible along the way. We definitely have that choice. If for some reason we had taken three cars, we still would have had fun and we would have made the most of it. It would have been different, but it still would have been a journey. Even though it may not have been the ideal situation, we would have made the best of it. Still, with that seemingly less-than-perfect method of travel, there would have been some benefits that would not have been available to us using the bus method. When we look for benefits, we will find them. The same is true in whatever journey you are on.

If you are intending to lose (release) five, ten, twenty, or one hundred pounds, there is always more than one path leading to that result. Even though the path you may be on is not to your taste, there are benefits on that path if you look for and appreciate them. When you do appreciate those benefits, you'll not only find them—you will enjoy them. Isn't life and everything we are striving for along the way all about enjoyment? My guess is most people would say yes!

Why do you want your ideal body? For you to look good? For you to feel good? What will that mean to you? Will people respect you or love you more? Will you have more energy and be healthier? What would that mean to you? Would you enjoy yourself more? What would the ideal life mean to you?

Be Grateful for the Past

Being grateful is very important and is a great habit to acquire. **The more you *appreciate* everything in your life, the more you are given.** To accelerate your success, you must appreciate the progress you are making and all of your accomplishments to date. You may consider reflecting back on your past and writing down all of your accomplishments—big and small. Then, appreciate each and every one of them. Appreciate the challenges, which are helping you grow and evolve. Take a few minutes to reflect on your past and write down all of your prior big challenges. Note how they benefited you. When you look deeply, you will find the benefit. Challenges make you stronger. When you truly feel gratitude in your heart, you are sending a huge force out into the universe that aids in the accomplishment of your desires. Appreciate.

How to Incorporate Gratitude

Whether or not you have ever been exposed to the concept of *gratitude*, this is a reminder. When you put it into practice on a regular basis, this simple idea of gratitude is worth a thousand times more than what you paid for this book. "How can I put it to use?" you ask. Being grateful is simply a decision to find the good and give thanks for it. Following are a few ideas that I found helpful:

Every morning, before my feet hit the floor, I say "thank you." Initially, these may be just words, but as you progress, add as many *feelings* or positive emotions as you can. Try to *feel* your gratitude. How can you tell if you have enough emotion? If a tear comes to your eye, you are there. Of course, there are many levels of gratitude, and to be at the point of weeping is definitely an intense level. You don't necessarily need to be at the point of weeping. Ideally, you should be at a point at which you can feel the emotion of gratitude.

I confess that sometimes in the morning, when I first woke up at 5 a.m., adding emotions—let alone weeping—wasn't really happening for me, especially when I first began this habit. However, at the end of a current day, when I watch our kids sleep and talk to them while they sleep, it is a lot easier for me to add those emotions. It has been made easier because I am awake and I am truly grateful for their being in my life.

That is not to say that I weep every time I tuck my kids in—because I don't. **The point is to be grateful.** We can be grateful from the moment we wake until the moment we drift off to sleep. When we express gratitude, we are more in line with our Higher Self, and when we are in such alignment, we allow the good to flow to us more easily.

My suggestion is to look for things—big and small—for which to be grateful. As you go through your day becoming more grateful, you will be more aware of other things to be grateful for. At this point, your increased awareness is a cause for inspired celebration. Gratitude is on par with *awareness* and *celebration*, which are both subsequent topics *in this important process.* When you are aware, you are in the present moment, and the present moment is our most powerful time.

TEACHING POINTS

- ☑ Be grateful for your efforts, challenges, and results.
- ☑ You must be grateful for your current state before it will improve.
- ☑ Be grateful during the journey.
- ☑ Be grateful for the past.
- ☑ You incorporate gratitude simply by deciding to find the good and then being thankful for it.

"If you change the way you look at something, the thing you look at changes."

—Dr. Wayne Dyer

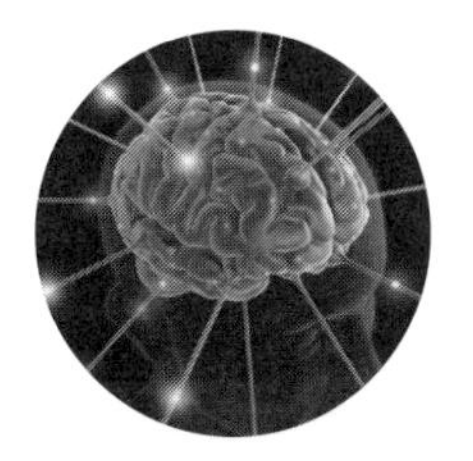

CHAPTER 15

Celebrate

> "He is a wise man who does not grieve for the things which he has not, but rejoices for those which he has."
>
> **—Epictetus**

As you go through this process of creating new behaviors and thought patterns, it will require some effort, and at times it may be uncomfortable for you to do so. To keep doing these things that will help you progress, you must celebrate and reward yourself when you accomplish what you need to do.

As you progress, celebrate. It is another critical step. Most people do their best work when they receive praise. They may work harder or dig deeper for those pats on the back. Of course, the members in your accountability group can assist you in this too. It is also very important for you to congratulate yourself. When you make the slightest progress or take a step in the right direction, you MUST celebrate with praise and reward yourself. Celebrate your successes. The prize doesn't have to be fancy. You could jump up and down, smile, and say, "Oh yeah!" You can go out to dinner. Decide what will work for you and use it. The point is to acknowledge your success and be grateful for your triumph.

Rewards Are a Form of Celebrating

While—and before I began—writing this book, I had to *condition* myself for this project. With my schedule, there were days when I got up at 5 a.m. to write. In the past, this was not my ideal time to awaken. My natural rhythm is staying up late, getting to bed around midnight to 1 a.m. and then waking at 7 or 8 a.m. For me, to sit down and write for two hours at a time was a new habit I had to form. To develop this habit, I used the same reconditioning techniques I have been describing here. Because writing this book seemed like such a big undertaking, I also came up with a cunning plan to "bribe" myself to do it.

Each day, when I completed my daily writing, I rewarded myself with a small treat of dark chocolate or some reward, and at the end of the week, I rewarded myself with a forty-five minute massage. This was my way of celebrating my successes.

You might be wondering about my chocolate reward. You may be asking yourself, "He is talking about being healthy and yet he rewards himself with chocolate?" That is a great question. After reprogramming my mind, I switched to dark chocolate, which is healthier and has less sugar. In my opinion, having a treat occasionally is fine as long as I am fulfilling my exercise and nutrition requirements. **Life is meant to be enjoyed, and the entire point of this book is that if you are healthier, you can enjoy more of life.**

You may have heard it said that success breeds success or success follows success. When I celebrate, it makes the extra effort worthwhile. I am inspired to want to do more. I have raised the stakes in this endeavor because this project is something I have never done before, so my rewards are bigger than what I am used to giving myself. The rewards are out of my comfort zone, and that is OK because I am striving to make big rewards the norm. Also, more pleasure is derived than discomfort, because I particularly love to be pampered with a massage. Instead of dreading the effort, I look forward to it. As an added benefit, this process of writing has brought me closer to my higher consciousness, which is always good.

Celebrating Is a Carrot-Type of Motivation

We humans either move away from pain or we move toward pleasure. In the chapter on commitment, we talked about my contract with myself. I would rather do the work than look uncommitted to those I sent a copy of my contract to. That is moving away from pain. Add to that my commitment to pay each person who catches me faltering. I believe that my faltering would make me look weak, as if I couldn't stick to a project—and that is a certain amount of pain I want to avoid. These are all things I want to move away from.

On the positive side are the daily rewards of my piece of dark chocolate or a couple of organic cookies. These little things are my daily reward, which I do truly enjoy. As an added bonus, my weekly reward and celebration is my massage. For me, that massage is truly exciting, inspiring, and definitely worth the work required to "earn" it. You might ask if such carrot-type motivation works for smaller goals, and I say that it does.

In the beginning of my new life, I rewarded myself with the proverbial pat on the back, which worked great too. After a completed set at an exercise session, I would smile and congratulate myself. On the first day, I celebrated after I walked for 10 minutes! The next day, I celebrated for completing two days in a row and continued to celebrate and reward myself for the positive actions I took toward my target objectives.

Find rewards that work best for you. A simple pat on the back and a congratulatory smile in the mirror is a great start. You want your rewards to be complimentary. However, when you are intending to be fit and healthy, it would be unwise to reward yourself daily with a greasy cheeseburger and fries. In fact, that practice would send the wrong message to your brain. Use good common sense when picking your rewards. I used a small treat for writing this book and I used other treats for my exercise rewards.

Remember, **it is critical to celebrate**. When you celebrate, you are actually expressing your gratitude for your efforts, which will attract more positive effort to be grateful for. If you have ever worked for someone else, you know what I am talking about. When a supervisor appreciates and rewards you for your efforts, you are motivated to do more. Sometimes, just the appreciation is enough to inspire us to do more, to do a better job. Rewarding yourself is another step to ensure that you are moving in the right direction. Do not underestimate this power. Are you ready to enjoy a lifetime of your ideal body and your ideal health? For what additional goal are you striving? Are you prepared to do whatever it takes to reach your goal? If so, then you are well on your way to accomplishing your targets!

> "When the voice and the vision on the inside become more profound, clear, and loud than the opinions on the outside, you've mastered your life!"
>
> **—Dr. John F. DeMartini**

Failing Is a Normal Part of the Success-Achievement Process

To accomplish something you haven't done before or something no one has done before, you will most likely have to take bold action, to go where you have not gone before and take a risk. In this process, you may fall or you may trip. The falling and the tripping are natural parts of development and are actually essential to the learning process. For example, a child who is learning to walk falls more often than not. We all understand that falling is a normal and natural part of this process. Therefore, as we get older, why should learning anything else be different?

Celebrating Reduces the Pain of Failure, Temporary Defeat, or Falling

As a child takes a step, we celebrate, cheer, smile, and clap. This positive reinforcement encourages the child to risk falling to take that next step, to make another attempt. Can you see how important the celebration is in the process? Remember, there will be obstacles and there may be falls. It does not matter how many falls you take. What matters is that you get back up each time and then celebrate the lesson! No matter how large or seemingly small your attempts and successes may be, celebrate. If you made an attempt and you took action, celebrate, and when it is appropriate, reward yourself. After enough attempts, what you'll find is that those seemingly tough tasks get easier and the progress becomes smoother.

The entire process we are discussing is designed to achieve the goal of creating new habits. The reason we choose to create a habit is that habits are powerful. Habits are based in our subconscious minds. They run automatically with very little conscious effort on our part. Can you say "autopilot"?

The majority of the energy required is in getting the habit started. Then the habit does the work. Initially, creating a big snowball at the top of a mountain takes some effort, but once you get it big enough and roll it to the side of the mountain, you can push it over the edge and it will increase in size all by itself. We have gravity to help. Habits are somewhat like gravity, and the same idea applies with habits. This law is sometimes referred to as the Law of Gestation or the Law of Sowing and Reaping.

Before we let nature take its course, we must put in our effort to build a snowball. We must set the foundation for the behaviors we choose. We can do that by following the steps in this book and then taking action. By *application* and *implementation*, we create these habits. GOYA is the acronym for "get off your assets." Move your feet. Do something. Get going. Only when you get the airplane off the ground and clear of any obstacles can you let up on the throttle.

Where Most Programs Fail

Where I believe most "how to" books fall short is in the *application of the principles,* which coincides with the lack of a continuity program. Therefore, in the last chapter, I include a thirty-day plan of how to apply these ideas, which is exactly what you need to do to create the habits and behaviors you are striving to initiate. Also, I include a link to a Web page where you can sign up for a three-month email coaching program included free as a bonus with this book. That's a $297 value. This bonus adds a continuity facet to this process, which will be another critical factor in your success. Should you choose to extend your continuity program, we offer advanced and ongoing coaching support. **The last chapter is entirely about taking action**. We will talk about what actions to take and, essentially, a plan to accomplish the sometimes elusive process of creating an empowering habit. Before we do that, let us now talk about how to set goals properly.

Set Your Goals Properly and Celebrate Even More

Let's take two types of goals—one fitness related and one a sales example—so that you can learn how to apply this process to other areas of your life. Let's say you weigh "X" and you want to weigh "Y" because it is healthier, you will feel better and have more energy, and you will look better. In this example, the numbers of pounds are not important. What is important is that you know your target and where you are starting. Take my example: I weighed around 216 pounds and my target goal was 195. When I achieved my target of 195, I decided I wasn't at my ideal weight and adjusted that goal. I lowered the target to 190, which I soon reached. You'll need to find out which weight is best for you. You'll feel better at a certain weight, which will be your ideal or target weight.

When I started, I knew where I was and I knew where I was going. I knew my "X" and my "Y." The only question was "How am I going to get there?" It was obvious that I needed to adjust my lifestyle. I needed to increase exercise and incorporate proper eating habits. The big question was how would I be able to persist until I got to my target weight? When I set my goal to exercise every day, it was controllable by me, and it would lead to my ultimate objective of weight reduction to reach my ideal weight and good health.

It was easy to ask myself at the end of the day, "Did I exercise today? Did I eat healthy foods today? What can I improve?" At the end of the day, I either did or I did not do what was required. Set up parameters when you start, and if you're not meeting those parameters, adjust your actions as you go, so that you stay on track.

As you get more in alignment with your intention, you will attract more information, which will help you along the way (Law of Attraction). I attracted an exercise and nutrition home study course into my life, which I read, bought into, and implemented. It opened my eyes to numerous new concepts I hadn't yet adopted. Many of these ideas are now a part of my regular thinking and everyday life. When, for the first time, I finished reading the material for that course, I realized that this information was exactly what I had been waiting for. Interestingly, the fitness and nutrition course had not appeared until I got started moving in the direction of my goal.

The important thing is that the goal I set was measurable. In my case, my goal was to exercise every day, and I set the parameter to exercise a minimum of thirty minutes a day. What this meant was that I needed to exercise EVERY DAY for thirty minutes. My intention wasn't to compete for a Tour de France. It was simply to exercise every day and offer my body some sort of break on my rest days with a *rest* version of exercise. For me, a rest day is a less intense day or a moderate session of exercise, which is acceptable to let the body recuperate and recover. However, I still wanted to get my body moving on that day, and my intention wasn't to exercise as intensely as seven-time Tour de France winner Lance Armstrong. It was to be fit, lean, and healthy.

> "The more you praise and celebrate your life, the more there is in life to celebrate."
>
> **—Oprah Winfrey**

Set Task-Oriented Daily Goals

Many fitness trainers encourage their clients to skip days, to exercise every other day, or to switch muscle groups. There is validity in this philosophy, and I agree that you do not want to exercise the same muscle group intensely day after day without rest between. However, we are now in the process of building a habit, which requires application *every day*, so this method needs to be modified for our habit-building process to be effective.

Can you see now why only 5% of people succeed with a weight loss and exercise program? Skipping days is one of the main reasons many people fail in their endeavor to build a habit.

To create an ironclad habit, the action you chose to turn into a habit needs to happen *every day*—without fail. I am not a doctor or a medical professional. However, it has been my experience that if you include light days or rest days while still doing *some* exercise with reduced intensity, your body will get the rest it needs and it will still be able to rebuild itself. Perhaps you will lift weights (or do some type of resistance training) two to three times a week, mixed with a few days of interval training and then go for a nice, casual walk the alternating two, three, or four times a week.

You do not want to exercise the same muscle group with great intensity two days in a row, so the muscles can rest and rebuild. On the other hand, you *can* exercise every day if you do it properly. I have exercised every day for over four years without any major injuries. If you hurt yourself, how are you going to exercise? I use my best judgment and practice exercising safely to keep myself healthy, so that I *can* exercise every day. The idea is to be fit and healthy, and injuries do not belong in that program!

It is always advisable to get professional advice from a health care provider before you start any exercise program.

Author's note: my attorney suggested that I include the previous statement.

If you remember, I started my exercise program with ten minutes of walking. Believe me, it wasn't a fast pace, either. It was a small miracle that I was able to use the treadmill. As I progressed and got up to "full speed," I incorporated other types of exercise, such as lifting weights, yoga, hockey, ice skating, in-line skating, biking, hiking, plyometrics, jumping (on a trampoline), and running. Every week, I include two to three rest days, when I simply go for a walk or do some other less intense exercise. I simply alternate exercising different muscle groups so that my body gets the rest it needs. **The goal you choose to set needs to be measurable and actionable.** My goal was to exercise every day for a minimum of thirty minutes. What is your goal?

These Principles Are Applicable Outside of the Fitness Realm

So that you can see how these strategies can be applied in other areas of your life, we now jump to a goal outside of health and fitness for a general explanation. If a salesperson wanted to make more sales, how could she use this process to create habits to improve her income? That is a great question. If a salesperson has decided to make "X" dollars and previously made only "Y" dollars, there is no way that she will make "X" dollars until she stops doing "Y" behavior and starts exhibiting "X" behavior. That is a natural law (cause and effect).What you put in, you get out. As you sow, so shall you reap. **There are certain patterns of thoughts, feelings, and actions—or behaviors and habits—that need to be changed to reach that goal.** If the salesperson wants to continue to earn the same amount, no major changes need to be made. To improve on that income, it will require making some changes—many of which may be known or unknown at the time the goal is set.

When the new goal is set with commitment, and effort is exerted toward the fulfillment of that goal, then methods and/or ideas will miraculously begin to appear. It is actually pretty cool to watch this phenomenon transpire. For instance, the salesperson can obviously set the goal of earning $100,000 annually when she is currently earning $50,000. The goal is clear and measurable, but there isn't a *specific action* described. Because she now calls twenty people a day to earn $50,000, based on the numbers, she will have to call forty people daily to achieve the new goal.

You might ask, "Why doesn't she just call forty people?" That solution seems simple, right? Yes, it seems simple. Remember, we humans will not out-perform our mental conditioning for sustained periods of time until we reprogram or recalibrate our internal mental program. That is why we are talking about setting goals in a certain way so that we can recalibrate our minds.

Her *goal statement* may be, "I call forty people every day." This is something she can measure, and she can ask herself, "Did I make forty prospecting calls today?" From this question, our salesperson can answer either yes or no. If she does make those calls and doesn't make the goal, she did her part and now must adjust the method or path to achievement. She will either need to increase the number of calls or improve her sales skills to increase the closing ratio. The point is, she is on track and can make adjustments.

There may be some thought required to determine the exact strategy to accomplish a particular goal. Seek and you will find. Can you see how the goal is measurable and actionable? Our salesperson's ultimate goal is to earn $100,000. To get there, in this example, the behavior and habit of calling forty people a day needs to be created and implemented.

If a person intends to improve a relationship with someone in his life, that is not currently measurable or actionable. Therefore, the goal will need to be phrased in the proper manner. **It is important to make sure that the goal is phrased so that it is *actionable* and *measurable*.**

He could say, "I spend an extra one hour a week with Susie." If, in the past, he spent two hours weekly with Susie, he would now choose to spend three hours with her. That goal is actionable and measurable. It could be stated like this, "I spend three hours a week with Susie." Of course, when you involve another person, goal-setting gets a little more complicated because there is that uncontrollable element. In this case, it is the other person. Maybe Susie doesn't have the extra time for him or their schedules conflict. You may want to phrase your goal to incorporate those possibilities, not as a way out, but only to clarify what is required of you daily. When you are considering doing your part, be sure that your goal statement includes, "I call on," "I visit," or whatever you can do that is measurable.

We are creating habits either on purpose or by default, and it is inevitable that your habits produce certain results. With some effort and an understanding of the principles in this book, we can control or change our habits to meet the new results we seek. Incorporating new habits requires some reprogramming and action. Hence, a new habit will be formed and the result will follow. Chapter 18 contains an action plan that will help you in the perpetual process of creating new habits.

TEACHING POINTS

- ☑ Celebrating is rewarding yourself for taking action.
- ☑ Celebrating increases the likelihood that you will act.
- ☑ Failing or falling down is a normal part of succeeding.
- ☑ Setting goals properly increases success and requires more celebrating.
- ☑ Set action goals for tasks you can do every day.
- ☑ These principles and strategies can be applied in any area of your life.

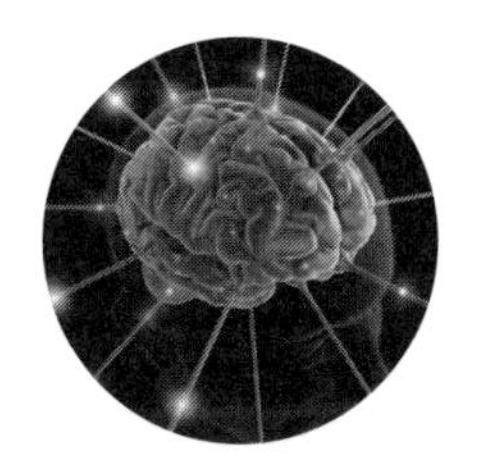

CHAPTER 16

Awareness

"The ultimate value of life depends upon awareness and the power of contemplation rather than upon mere survival."

—Aristotle

Awareness is being attuned to what is going on within and around you. The main reason you want to be aware is so you see and capitalize on opportunities when they present themselves. You also must make sure that your thoughts, words, and actions—and those within your environment—are leading you toward your goals. Furthermore, we must make sure to test if something is moving you toward your goal or moving you away from it. Ask yourself, "Is this thought, word, feeling, or action bringing or moving me closer to my goal, or is it taking me further away?"

There is no middle ground. You are either going *toward* or you are going *away from* your goal. What you'll soon learn is that everything counts. Is it moving you closer to your goal or away? The answer will determine whether you should continue to engage in that activity or whether you should choose a different activity or environment. It all starts with awareness. When you have ANTs and you're not aware that they are there, they can haul away your picnic.

The following table contains three major areas to be consciously aware of on an ongoing basis. Keeping a sharp eye on these areas is critical to your success.

Your	Others'	Your Environment
words	words	radio, music, TV shows, commercials
thoughts	actions	clubs, organizations
feelings	emotions	neighborhoods
actions	habits	religious organizations

This concept is not just limited to you. It also relates to the people around you. You want to be aware of the people around you because they definitely have an impact on your behavior. **Everything affects everything else.** Be aware of people's words, actions, and emotions. Ask yourself, "Is this (stimulus) helping me move toward my target, or is it moving me away from my target?"

If the people around you are not "good" for you, you will then need to make a decision. Bob Proctor, a mentor of mine, says, "You don't have to divorce them. Just don't go as often and don't stay as long." If you are around people or in an environment that sucks the life out of you, how can you expect to thrive? There are lessons here. Pay attention. People who suck the life force out of you are helping themselves, not you! Some call these people psychic vampires.

If you are striving to achieve bigger goals, you'll need to limit—if not eliminate—your contact with such people and stay away from environments that are not conducive to positive growth or encouragement. Remember, we have been conditioned by our environments. It is easy to maintain old, bad, or nonproductive habits when you remain in the same old environment where they were spawned.

If we are now succeeding with our new goals, then it is important to stay in those environments that help produce the actions, behaviors, and results you desire. As your old environment conditioned you, so will your new environment. At this point, you know more about that process, you are more aware, and you are able to better facilitate your new conditioning.

A Different Fish Tale

Be aware. Understand where you are and what effect your environment is having on you. I am not saying to use your environment as an excuse. Ultimately, your environment is your responsibility. However, understanding and knowing your environment does play an important role in gaining success. Think of a fish for a moment. It is swimming around in a body of water and doesn't even know it is in the water until it is pulled out of the water. If it gets caught by a fisherman and is reeled out of the water and into the air, then it suddenly realizes, "Hey, where is the water?" At that time, it longs to get back into the water for the sake of survival.

We'll call this fish Freddy. Let's say Freddy was born and raised in an area where the sea was polluted. Because Freddy grew up in this water, he doesn't know the water is polluted. He has lived there since he was a little egg and he knows no other environment. He and his family swim around, stay within a certain area (comfort zone), and never venture out very far. He doesn't know any different and, to Freddy, the polluted water is normal, comfortable, and fine.

All is good until one day Freddy the fish is caught by some kids. They reel him in and put him into a bucket of clean salt water. At first, Freddy is jolted because of the contrast between the water from which he came and the water in which he now finds himself. He is currently confined to a small bucket, and he is definitely out of his comfort zone.

As the boys finish fishing and speed off in their boat from Freddy's home under the sea, they hit some big waves, and the bucket holding Freddy falls into the water. Freddy swims out of the bucket and into the freedom of the ocean. Now Freddy is free, but he is lost. He is in an entirely new environment. The nearby fish seem happier, more alive, and even more colorful.

Then, Freddy notices that the water here is different—not polluted. It is cleaner and fresher tasting. It is even easier to breathe. It feels different, and in an odd way, it feels richer than the water where he was raised. The fish in this area are friendlier. They smile, introduce themselves, and are very social. Freddy almost feels at home, even though everything seems strange in his new surroundings. There is a huge, magnetic-like pull drawing Freddy back to his own, familiar waters (comfort zone/environment).

At the same time, Freddy loves this new, cleaner water he is now in. One of his first thoughts is to swim back "home" to tell all of his friends and family about this clean area and these new waters. Sadly, he knows deep down that they probably will not believe him. Moments ago, he was caught on a fishing line. Now he is caught in a predicament. Should he go back to his friends and family, or should he stay here? This decision will determine the rest of his life and may even determine the length of his life.

The pollution in this story is a metaphor and could represent a number of things in your life, such as unhealthy foods, habits, negative people, TV, radio, movies, magazines, and newspapers. We are all faced with similar challenges. Once we become aware that we are in polluted waters, we need to decide whether we're going to stay in that place or move to a better environment with fresher waters.

Become Aware of Your Comfort Zone

Some people may never take the opportunity to become aware of the pollution in their lives. It may be all they have ever known, and even though they may not like it, it is a comfort zone that they are used to. As children, we have a very small comfort zone; usually, it is right beside our parents. Maybe we even held a parent's leg in the presence of strangers. I know I did. As we grow, we step further away from our parents, and our comfort zone expands. With every exploratory step we take, the larger our new zone becomes. The bigger it is, the more we are able to experience in life. **The challenge is to become aware that we are in a comfort zone.** When we are in polluted water, we need to swim or step out of that pollution. Freddy was caught and jolted out of his comfort zone. Now, let me tell you about one of Freddy's friends named Roger.

Expand Your Comfort Zone

Roger was an early adopter, and he tried new things. He liked adventure and he expanded his comfort zone earlier than most fish. Not only did he venture out earlier, he expanded the size of his zone more than most fish. For quite some time, Roger had been telling Freddy about the outskirts of the waters where they lived. Roger told him it was nicer, cleaner, and more vibrant with colors in this new location. Unfortunately, Freddy never believed his friend, so he remained in the comfort zone of his home waters.

On the other hand, Roger kept expanding his own comfort zone daily, until it took an entire day to swim to the edge of his newly discovered location. Roger was getting so comfortable with the cleaner water that he actually began to feel dirty when he swam back home. Eventually, Roger spent more time in the clean water; it became *his new comfort zone,* and he rarely went back to his old zone. Finally, one day, he decided that he was never going to breathe dirty water again, and he never went back to his old home.

Of these two characters, which one do you think has a greater likelihood of succeeding in his new environment? Yes, Roger will. Of course, Freddy may do so as well *if* he *embraces* the new feelings that he will experience being in this new water (new environment).

There is another fish in this story, and his name is Norman. This fish likes everything to stay the same. He actually thought Roger was crazy—off his rocker and maybe a freak. Norman lived a "normal" life in the security of his environment, not aware that there was any other possibility. He was comfortable being miserable. Norman didn't believe that a place of cleaner water existed or that he could ever get to such a place. He breathed his polluted water in and out and would continue to do so unless something drastic happened. Most likely, he would never be aware that a real alternative existed.

We all know people who emulate at least one of these characters. My question is: Which one would you want to be? Do you want to stay where you are in ignorance? Would you rather wait for chance or luck to determine your future? Or, do you want to venture out to learn of new fresher and cleaner waters filled with new life?

What are you aware of now? What could you become more aware of? Scientists tell us that our brains are taking in over six billion bits of information every second and that we are only consciously aware of about two thousand bits per second. Most of those bits of information that we *are* aware of have to do with our comfort level and our environment. When you attend one of my live events, you can participate in a few different exercises that perfectly illustrate this point. Sometimes things might be right in front of your face, yet you may not see them. You aren't aware.

"What is necessary to change a person is to change his awareness of himself."

—Abraham Maslow

My intention is to pique your curiosity, which will perhaps get you looking at things differently. Moreover, the impact of these exercises is reduced significantly when you read about them versus actually experiencing them. That is true with most learning experiences, because the real learning takes place when we experience it for ourselves. Books are wonderful because a book can be the beginning of an entirely new understanding. **The power is in the application.** That is why, at the end of this book, there is an entire chapter dedicated to putting all these ideas into a daily, ongoing experience.

Here are some things to become more aware of—self, others, and the environment:

Self: The personal thoughts you have, the words you use daily, the feelings you experience, and the actions you consistently take.

Thoughts-	Are they positive? ANTs—do you have any automatic negative thoughts? Are you aware of your ANTs? Are you eliminating them?
Words-	Are they focused on what you want or what you don't want? Are they positive or negative? Are they moving you toward your goal? What words are you consistently using?
Feelings-	What emotions do you feel most frequently? How do you feel? Are your feelings serving you?
Actions-	What actions are you taking? What actions are you NOT taking? Are you exercising? What and how much are you eating?

Others: With whom are you spending the most time, and what are the words they use, the emotions they express, and the actions they take on a consistent basis?

Words-	Are they positive or negative? What words do they use most frequently?
Emotions-	Are these people positive or negative? What kind of emotions do they express frequently?
Actions-	What actions do they take? Are they positive or negative? What are they eating and drinking? Are they exercising? What type of exercise are they doing?

Environment: This label does include other people, but because we have "Others" as a separate category, *here* environment includes everything else surrounding you.

TV, Radio-	What kind of television programming is in your environment? Are the people in your environment watching television? What types of shows are they watching? Are they positive or negative shows? What kind of music are you listening to?
Movies-	What kind of movies are you watching?
Institutions-	What kind of establishments do you spend your time in? Church, temple, synagogue, clubs, other organizations?
Schools-	What are they teaching?
Work-	Is it a positive or negative environment?
Home-	Is it a loving and supportive environment?
Books-	Are you reading books? Are they positive, educational, or motivational? Are they adding to your life? Are they moving you closer to your goals?
Other-	What kind of educational DVD and CD programs do you expose yourself to? How often?
Seminars-	What kinds of programs are you attending that add to your life? How often?

Examining your environment is critical to facilitating your success—not only examining it. **I invite you to upgrade yourself.** If changes need to be made in certain areas to ensure the shifts you desire, you will need to make certain changes in your environment.

> "A problem cannot be solved at the same level in which the problem was created."
>
> **—Albert Einstein**

Knowing the Path Is Different from Taking the Path

Knowing (being aware of) your environment is one thing; making changes within that environment is another. You will be faced with some tough decisions, and these decisions will determine what path you will travel. Once you consciously begin to develop this awareness, you'll start to "see" things that may have been there all along that you were not aware of.

We see with our mind, not our eyes. Have you ever misplaced something, such as your car keys? You may have looked everywhere and you couldn't seem to find them. In fact, you may have looked in the same place a half-dozen times, thinking you missed them in your previous search. You may even think to yourself or tell others "I can't find my keys," or "I don't see my keys anywhere." These statements are *negative affirmations* or *negations*. Perhaps you may get slightly upset and feel frustration and/or anxiety.

These emotions may be exaggerated, especially if you are running late for an appointment. Eventually, you will find your keys, and what is strange is that they were right where you looked three or four times, but you didn't see them. You saw them with your eyes, but you didn't see them with your mind. For whatever reason, you blocked seeing your keys. When you relaxed, you were able to see them. They were there all along, even though you could not observe them.

As you progress, you want to become more aware, and your environment, which includes you, is a great place to start to increase your awareness. Your environment includes the friends you keep, your coworkers, and the areas of your life that are less tangible. These less tangible areas include the words you use and the language patterns of all people and organizations around you. Words are powerful! Be aware of words. Thoughts precede words. Tune in to your thoughts. You can control your thoughts, but first you must be aware of them.

Remember that experts calculate that we entertain fifty to sixty thousand thoughts every single day. Eighty percent of our thoughts are the same five to seven thoughts, so we are thinking a few thoughts over and over again. We need to be aware of what we are thinking, speaking, and hearing from others. Then, we need to ask ourselves if those thoughts or ideas are going to move us toward our goals or move us away from them. Be aware of your surroundings because you may need to make some changes (decisions).

Along with awareness, *continually increasing our understanding* is the next topic we'll discuss. I believe that understanding is essential for conscious, continued growth. That means always increasing your understanding and wisdom through reading, writing, and studying. Studying can be done through a number of avenues, such as books, CDs, videos, seminars, workshops, boot camps, and just living life and paying attention.

TEACHING POINTS

- [x] Awareness is being attuned to what is occurring internally and externally.
- [x] Three major areas to concern yourself with are:
  - [x] yourself
  - [x] others
  - [x] the environment
- [x] If you are always in a given environment, you may not be aware of its negatives.
- [x] Become aware of your comfort zone.
- [x] To grow you must expand your comfort zone.
- [x] Awareness entails making observations about yourself, such as your:
  - [x] thoughts
  - [x] feelings
  - [x] words
  - [x] actions
- [x] Awareness involves observing things about others, such as:
  - [x] words
  - [x] emotions
  - [x] actions
- [x] Awareness requires observing things about your environment, such as:
  - [x] tv, radio, movies
  - [x] schools, institutions
  - [x] work, home
  - [x] books, CDs, DVDs, seminars, events

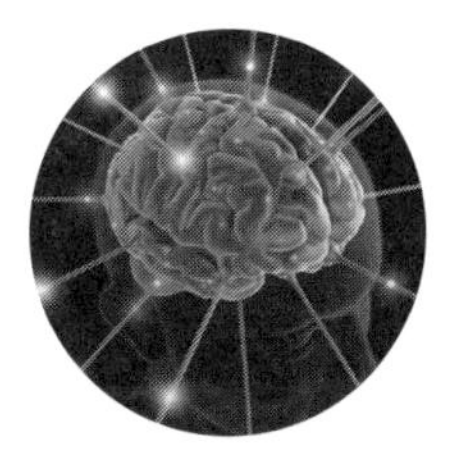

CHAPTER 17

Increasing Understanding

"Everyone hears only what he understands."

—Johann Wolfgang von Goethe

If you are not growing, you are dying. When you are learning, you are growing. Technically, we are always growing and evolving, although we are often doing so unconsciously. It is important to strive consciously and to grow continuously—pushing the envelope of your own personal growth. As you seek, so shall you find. Knock and the door will be opened to you. When you are striving for growth and wisdom, more of both will be made available to you.

Sometimes, when I am coaching someone, I use the golf ball and basketball analogy to illustrate this point. If you have a golf ball-sized understanding, you will only receive a golf ball-sized lesson from a book, class, program, or experience. However, if you have a basketball-sized understanding, you will receive a basketball-sized lesson. **Your lessons are determined by the *size* of your own consciousness or understanding.**

Therefore, keep striving to grow and thrive. Increasing our understanding also affects our awareness. In my opinion, it is fun to learn and grow. Some people don't agree. However, I believe that I now have reached a certain level of understanding, which opens certain doors of success. Patience may be needed because new lessons sometimes take time to embrace.

There are many ways to increase your understanding. I have consistently benefited from reading and studying books, listening to educational programs on CDs, and watching DVDs. I also invest in home-study courses; participate in seminars, conferences, and live educational programs; and I attend networking events. There are other previously mentioned things that I do, such as hiring and working with a coach or studying under a mentor, getting involved in a mastermind group, or working with an accountability buddy. This is by no means a complete list, but it gives you a starting point.

Those are all ways to increase your understanding on an accelerated basis. At times, your progress and understanding may not *seem* to be advancing as quickly as you would like, and here is where *patience* is necessary.

Books Are Your Friends

Since you are reading this book, you are already on the proper path regarding books. Congratulations! Also, I would like to take a moment to commend you, as you've made it this far in this book. Surprisingly, over half of new books are not read to completion. Another big acknowledgment is in order if this is your second or third time reading this book. You are among an elite few. The percentage of people who read a book more than once is considerably smaller than for those who read a book only once. Those people who read a book more than once will gain the most benefits.

If this is your first reading, consider making the decision to commit to a second reading immediately following your first reading.

If you are reading this book for the second or third time, you are most assuredly elite in your desire to understand and master these concepts, and I applaud you. I suggest that you consider investing in an additional copy of this book for a friend and getting him or her involved in fitness and well-being. You and your friend can then be accountability buddies for each other.

There may be certain subjects that will be more interesting to you than others. Be sure to read whatever you find of interest in the personal development arena. I have learned and grown so much from reading books. Last year, my target goal was to read an average of one book a week. That is fifty-two books a year.

"The man who does not read good books has no advantage over the man who cannot read them."

—Mark Twain

Even if you read a book a year, you are reading more than most people—not that you are competing with others. Likewise, if you opted for a book per month, that is twelve books a year, and in ten years, you will have read 120 books. Those 120 books have the potential to help you in many areas of your life. The books I encourage you to read are books on *personal development or business*, not romance novels or vampire books. I'm talking about *educational, inspirational, motivational, and biographical books*, which will educate and inspire you. Additionally, career, business, or industry-specific books can add value and help advance your career.

Furthermore, books on your hobby or interests can add fun to your life. **Read books that add value to your life.** The *value* I'm referring to is in books that *upgrade* your life. Remember, the books you read are part of your environment, so when you pick a book, choose wisely.

> "You will be the same person in five years as you are today except for the people you meet and the books you read."
>
> —Charles "Tremendous" Jones

CDs, DVDs, and Home-Study Programs Are Great Learning Tools

I own CDs, DVDs, and home-study programs that I feel are outstanding. One, in particular, I listen to three to four times a year. One is a classic program with some timeless content, which I choose to keep in my environment to reinforce and remind me of powerful ideas. With current technology, we are able to put these audiovisual programs on our video MP3 players and mobile phones. We can listen or watch on the go, whenever we choose. This is a great opportunity to capitalize on time and put some great content into our minds.

For years, I have used my car as a university on wheels by listening to audio books and audio programs. During my drives to work or school, I still choose to listen to educational, motivational, and spiritual programs instead of listening to the radio. Years ago, I used to say proudly that I learned more life-impacting ideas in my car on the way to and from my college classes by listening to tapes and CDs than I learned in the classrooms. I know that to be true. I'm not saying that I didn't learn life-impacting ideas in college, but I definitely learned more via audio programs.

Invest in Yourself by Attending Seminars and Conferences

I love attending meaningful events, especially seminars and conferences. They require a financial investment considerably more than a book, CD, or DVD program, but the benefits you get from being there live and interacting with the presenter(s) and other attendees are invaluable. This is especially true when a good deal of the content is interactive.

Sometimes, you may get to fly to another city to attend these events. One advantage of an out-of-town event is that it gets you out of your regular environment and allows you to focus more on the event, without many of the routine interruptions popping up. The friendships I have made attending these events are priceless, and I will cherish them forever! **The best investment you can ever make is an investment in yourself, your personal development, and your education.**

> "An investment in knowledge always pays the best interest."
>
> **—Benjamin Franklin**

Find the right quality and quantity of events to attend each year. If you are in a state of over-learning and seldom implementing these new ideas, you may want to consider cutting back. Currently, with all I am doing and the types of events I attend—usually two to four days long—the ideal quantity is four to five events a year or one event per quarter. If the seminar or conference is a one- or two-day event, I can increase the frequency. "Seminar junkies," who attend event after event but do not implement the ideas, are fooling themselves into thinking that attending large quantities of events will fix their problems. Mixing fewer events with massive implementation is a more productive model for increasing understanding.

Last year, as a participant, I attended several events, including three events that were each one month apart. They were great, and I loved attending them. However, I did not utilize as much of the content of one event—even though I did benefit—because of timing. Unfortunately, after I returned from one event, I was getting ready to go to another. They were too close together, and I didn't make the time to debrief one of the programs.

Debriefing is critical. It is putting information into implementation. *Application or augmentation is where all the benefits lie.* When I debrief, I go over all my notes and rewrite them, and then I pick the top three ideas I want to implement in the current month. Thirty days later, I go to my notes and locate the next top three ideas. This is a great way for me to put what I learned to work, provided I have done a debriefing and prioritized the top ideas to be implemented.

I also use this debriefing process with books I like. I write down the top three ideas from each chapter. Then, I implement them to the best of my ability.

When attending seminars and conferences, you will need to determine what timing and frequency works best for you. At a minimum, I suggest setting a goal to attend at least one multi-day seminar or learning conference a year. I believe that the benefits you will reap from a quality self-improvement or business seminar will far outweigh the money you invest to get there.

Of course, I encourage you to attend one of our upcoming events. For more information concerning our upcoming seminars, visit www.donstaley.com/speaking/live-events.

Finally, you will increase your understanding by implementing all of the ideas mentioned in this book and by reading, studying, and working with a coach to learn more. We don't have to learn it all, and we certainly don't have to learn it all now. However, we do want to keep growing and evolving! I know you do too. Otherwise, you wouldn't be reading this book. Reading books and articles is one of numerous ways to learn.

There are many ways to gather information to increase your understanding. The best way is through *application* and *implementation.* In the book *Harmonic Wealth: The Secret of Attracting the Life You Want,* author James Arthur Ray talks about going three for three; thoughts, feelings, and actions. Taking action on the ideas in this book greatly increases your understanding. At first, these ideas may appear to be merely theories, and to you, perhaps they still are. However, rest assured that they are more than theories. These concepts work! I and countless others have proved this to be true. I have used and tested everything in this book and I still use many of these ideas. In fact, they have helped me to advance to the next level of success along my path.

In certain areas of my life, I have been able to pull back or ease off the throttle. The interesting thing is that the more you learn and understand, the more you want to learn and understand. Knowledge feeds itself. We are always learning, and no one knows everything. Our path is living our lives and evolving our understanding. Enjoy the journey and this book. I not only believe it will help you, I KNOW it will! However, you must put these ideas to work. A book sitting on a shelf does nothing but look pretty until you open it up, read it, and—more importantly—apply it.

When put to work, all these ideas will surely be a great way to increase your understanding. This is a fast track to facilitate your progress down the path of personal success. Use what works for you, and you will have more reasons to celebrate.

TEACHING POINTS

- ☑ The more you learn and grow, the more you can learn and grow.
- ☑ There are many ways to increase your understanding. Some are:
  - ☑ books
  - ☑ CDs, DVDs, and MP3s
  - ☑ home-study courses
  - ☑ live events
  - ☑ seminars
  - ☑ conferences
- ☑ Books are quick and affordable methods of learning.
- ☑ CDs and MP3s can turn your idle or driving time into learning time.
- ☑ DVDs and home-study courses bring the learning to your home or office.
- ☑ Live events, seminars, and conferences are great learning events, where you meet like-minded friends.
- ☑ Debriefing learning tools is essential for better implementation.

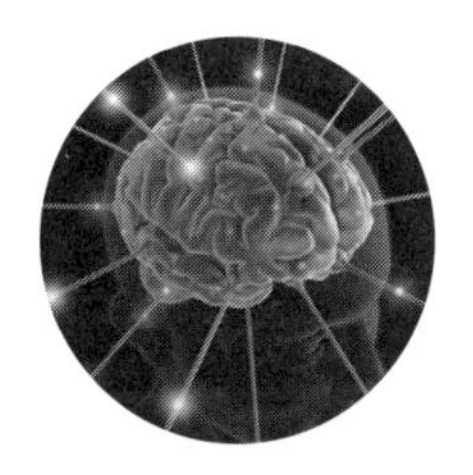

CHAPTER 18

Action Plan

"A good plan implemented today is better than a perfect plan implemented tomorrow."

—General George S. Patton

Using an action plan forces you to keep your goals in mind and to measure just how much you are implementing. Furthermore, some days require a lighter "take action load" than others, but they are all important.

DAY ONE

Check off these boxes as you complete each task.

- ❑ Take responsibility for past results by writing down a few in each category. (Example: I was lazy, lacked commitment and self-discipline, was overweight and/or out of shape, ate unhealthy foods, employed negative thoughts and programs.)
  - ❑ past thoughts________________________
  - ❑ past behaviors ______________________
  - ❑ past actions _________________________
  - ❑ past habits __________________________
- ❑ Take inventory—evaluate past beliefs
  - ❑ Weigh in
    - ❑ weight _____________ pounds
  - ❑ Measure

    waist_________, hips_________, chest_________,
    arms_________, thighs_________, calves_________,
    neck_________, shoulders _________,
    body fat percent_________
  - ❑ Take *before photos* (front, side, back)
  - ❑ Take responsibility for future results
- ❑ Sign responsibility agreement

Take Responsibility for the Past

Day one is about taking responsibility for your results. It requires a mind shift, if you haven't already made one. You MUST take personal responsibility for your success as well as your past failures. This means that you take responsibility for your thoughts, behaviors, actions, and habits. This also means ***you* are responsible for *your* results.** Some of the programs you currently have running your life are the results of years of programming (most likely from others), and you may not have understood the programming process back then. Maybe your being where you are now is not your fault because you didn't understand or realize just how much prior conditioning you've been exposed to. Now you do. Now, you know. **From this day on, it is *your* responsibility.**

TAKE INVENTORY

Take inventory of where your thoughts have led you up to this point in your life. Note that your present results are not revealing who you really are. They are a reflection of who you WERE.

Weigh In

Weigh yourself. Find an accurate scale, hop (gently) onto it, and mark down the results. No more excuses—these are results or effects from certain causes, and we are NOW changing those causes. You will transfer this data to your journal in an upcoming assignment. Remember, your present weight doesn't reflect who you are; it is indicating who you were.

Measure Body

Take your body measurements. This is another way to identify where your thoughts have led you. It will also act as a benchmark of where you have come from once you obtain your new fit, ideal body. These data serve as a stern reminder that your old thoughts, feelings, and actions delivered those results. **To avoid such results in the future, you must avoid those causes.** Remember, for every effect, there is a cause.

Measure Body-Fat Percentage

You will also want to take your body-fat percentage. If you have a body-fat percentage caliper, then you can take your own measurements.

Otherwise, go to a fitness or health club that measures body-fat percentage. As an alternative, you will need to get your hands on a device that you can use to take that measurement. If you are unable to get this done today, at the very least, you must schedule it on your calendar and make it happen within the next week.

Take *Before* Photos

Next, take your *before* photo. If you don't have a digital camera, you can buy a disposable camera at almost any store for a few dollars. This action needs to be completed today, and if that isn't possible, then make sure you schedule to get it done within the week. It will be easy to put these tasks off. You must get tough with yourself. In a loving way, make yourself do it and do it now. Are you doing whatever it takes?

To get where you are going, you need to know where you are. Once you know where you are, you can set a course to where you are going.

TAKE RESPONSIBILITY FOR THE FUTURE

Now it is up to you. If you are ever going to change your life, you must change the old programming. For different results, different programming is necessary. To get you where you want to go in the future, you must act now.

Sign Responsibility Agreement

To help secure your success, I have created a responsibility agreement. Read it, copy it, and print it. Sign and post it where you can see it on a regular basis. Now, get ready to enjoy newfound freedom, because when you take responsibility, you are shedding the shackles of excuses that have held you back for years. Congratulations!

Responsibility Agreement

I, ________________________________, am now taking full responsibility for the results in my life.

Ultimately, I control my results, and if I choose to have different results from my current results, I understand that I must commit to making changes to my thoughts and behaviors. Even though I can make conscious decisions to move in the direction of my new goals, I also understand that expediting the process of creating new habits does require reconditioning of my mind, body, and spirit to be in harmony with my new intentions. It is up to me. I am responsible, and from this day forward, I am the only one responsible for my results.

Truly,

____

Signed

DAY TWO

Check off these boxes as you complete each task.

- ❑ Sign binding agreement of personal commitment
- ❑ Buy journal or notebook
- ❑ Transfer body measurement data to journal
- ❑ Fantasize about your ideal body
- ❑ Note your thoughts in journal

SIGN BINDING AGREEMENT OF PERSONAL COMMITMENT

Having now signed the responsibility pledge, you have taken personal responsibility for your actions and your results, which means you understand that your success is totally up to you. You have eliminated the crutch of *blaming*, and you can now let your desire surface.

It is now time to commit to put forth every effort to the accomplishment of your goal. To chase down this dream requires you to be 100% committed to the accomplishment of this aspiration.

When we borrow money to buy a house or car, our commitment is required to affirm that we are going to pay it back. This commitment is usually in the form of our signature on a contract or an agreement. Accordingly, I have prepared a binding agreement of personal commitment. If you are ready, commit to yourself. Do it now!

Binding Agreement of Personal Commitment with Me, Myself, and I

I, ________________________________, the undersigned, commit and agree to furnish all material, effort, and labor necessary to design and create my IDEAL LIFE or the LIFE OF MY DREAMS.

As a person of honesty and integrity, I hereby commit to doing WHATEVER it takes to achieve the greatness that I know is within me.

I now commit to pay the price with the discipline (versus paying later with regret) necessary to reach my life's dream and destiny because I know that not fulfilling my destiny will not only leave me feeling short-changed in my life but will leave the entire world short-changed as well.

I understand that the MY IDEAL LIFE DESIGN PLAN is to be reached one step at a time, with each step bringing me closer to MY IDEAL LIFE. I understand that there may be times when the results I am looking for may not be visible, but I am committed to keep moving forward.

From NOW on, I commit to settle only for achieving MY IDEAL LIFE or the LIFE OF MY DREAMS!

I have the power, I have the knowledge, and I have what it takes.

____
Signature

____
Date

BUY JOURNAL OR NOTEBOOK

Today, we are continuing the journey to your ideal body and, ultimately, to your ideal life. To track and record your journey, you will be assisted in this venture by the accompaniment of a journal or notebook.

You will use this journal or notebook for multiple purposes. Therefore, consider investing in something nice, as you will be carrying it with you. However, if you prefer, a spiral notebook will suffice.

Transfer Data to Journal

Yesterday, you took some body measurements. Transfer these data to your new journal or notebook. When you reach your goal, it will feel good and be nice to show people—as well as to remind yourself—where you started.

Transfer *all* the measurement data. If there is a number you still need to secure, get it done and write it down. Do it now!

FANTASIZE ABOUT YOUR IDEAL BODY

What is it you truly want to have in your life? What are you willing to trade your life for? **Each morning, life gives you 86,400 seconds. What you do with that precious time is exactly what you are "trading" your life for. Is the trade worth it?** If not, what has to happen for it to be worth it? Here is a cold, harsh fact: right now, you are giving your life for whatever you are doing, being, and having. If you allow yourself to be fat and out of shape, in essence, you are saying, "I give my life experience to be unfit."

When you find the answer to what you really want, that is your desire. What has to happen to make living your life *more* meaningful to you? Find your desire, and then you are ready for the next step. What do you choose to look like? What do you want to weigh? What body-fat percentage do you want? In the health and fitness realm, how do you want to feel? How much energy do you want? What is your ideal body like? **Think of this in terms of what you truly desire, not what you think you can achieve.**

Note Thoughts in Journal

Record your thoughts regarding your fantasy of your ideal life and ideal body. How did you feel while exploring the possibility of living in your ideal body? Were you inspired? Are you still inspired? Capture these thoughts in your journal. Take as much time as you need to record your thoughts and feelings.

DAY THREE

Check off these boxes as you complete each task.

- ❑ Ascertain your desire
  - ❑ Complete SEEQ (self evaluation & exploration questionnaire)
  - ❑ Note thoughts in journal

What Are Your Desires, Goals?

Day three is to be used for finding your desire or letting it surface. You may already know exactly what you want, or it may seem cloudy because you have been conditioned to believe that you do not deserve it. Regardless, let's conduct a personal evaluation and exploration to confirm your true desire.

This may seem simple enough, but it does require some soul-searching. To help facilitate this process, you can follow the basic form in this book, or to be more precise, you can follow the full version at:

www.donstaley.com/fitmindbook.

Self Evaluation & Exploration Questionnaire

1. Exactly what are you intending to accomplish (main fitness objective)?

2. Why must you have this in your life? (list 25 reasons)
   1. ______________________________
   2. ______________________________
   3. ______________________________
   4. ______________________________
   5. ______________________________

6. ______________________________
7. ______________________________
8. ______________________________
9. ______________________________
10. ______________________________
11. ______________________________
12. ______________________________
13. ______________________________
14. ______________________________
15. ______________________________
16. ______________________________
17. ______________________________
18. ______________________________
19. ______________________________
20. ______________________________
21. ______________________________
22. ______________________________
23. ______________________________
24. ______________________________
25. ______________________________

3. What are your top three goals/objectives?
    1. ______________________________
    2. ______________________________
    3. ______________________________

4. If you had a magic wand, what would your ideal life be like?

5. What do you want in your ideal life?

6. How will you feel when you have it?

What's Holding You Back?

7. What keeps you awake at night?

8. Regarding your goals, what are two or three primary habits you believe may be holding you back from achieving the results you desire?
   1. ______________________________
   2. ______________________________
   3. ______________________________

9. What changes/actions are needed for these to be accomplished easily?

10. What frustrates you?

11. What are you afraid of?

12. How many hours of television do you watch per day?
    Per week?

How Committed Are You?

13. Are you willing to do seemingly silly things to accomplish your goals?

14. Are you willing to do whatever* it takes to accomplish your objective?

15. How much time are you devoting to other activities (school, work, family, TV, sports, personal development, etc.)?

16. Are you willing to reduce the time you spend watching television each day and instead take time to create your ideal life?

17. How much time can you devote to this program daily?

    Weekly?

18. Are you willing to take before and after pictures?

**While being a person of honesty and integrity.*

This was a quick eighteen-question journey into your thoughts and beliefs. Did you notice any negative thoughts? What else did you notice? Great work! Now, go and record your experience of this assignment in your journal.

Note Thoughts in Journal

Record your thoughts regarding what came from the SEEQ. Have you been aware of this desire all along or are you now letting it rise to the surface? Were you able to come up with enough reasons that you must have this desire become a reality? Take as much time as you need to record your thoughts and feelings.

DAY FOUR

Check off these boxes as you complete each task.

- ❑ Make decision
- ❑ Begin search for ideal body photo

MAKE DECISION

Day four: The next step is to make a decision to have exactly what it is you choose to have as a part of your new life—your ideal life. What is the result you want? This could be an ideal weight, an ideal body-fat percentage, a certain look, or a certain level of fitness, such as running a mile in five minutes, having a resting heart rate of sixty beats per minute, being able to do one hundred situps in five minutes, etc., or simply to feel good. What do you desire?

To know what you choose to have in your new life may require more soul-searching. You may already know exactly what it is because you have been *trying* to get there for many years and/or you completed yesterday's assignment, and thus you uncovered it.

Now is the time to decide to have your desire be manifested. A real decision cuts off all the other possibilities. Once you make this possibly life-changing decision, you can move on to the next step.

Begin Search: Ideal Body Photo

Begin the search for your ideal body photo. You can do this in fitness catalogs. Any major bookstore will have a nice magazine section, so you can peruse through a variety of magazines until you find the photo or photos you want. Then, be willing to make the small investment for your new and ideal body by purchasing the magazine(s) with your photo(s). You can also conduct this search online, where there are millions of photos. If you need help with ideas on where to search, flip back to the section on visualizations in the chapter on reprogramming (chapter 12).

DAY FIVE

Check off these boxes as you complete each task.

- ❑ Getting absolute clarity
  - ❑ Write ideal life screenplay
    - ❑ physical / body
    - ❑ mental
    - ❑ spiritual
    - ❑ financial
    - ❑ relational
- ❑ Assemble ideal life area scripts

GETTING ABSOLUTE CLARITY

Day five: Once you decide on a goal or intention, it is important to crystallize it so that your vision is absolutely clear. Take a moment to look at what you have written down as your desire. At this point, you must know *exactly* what it is you want. Then, you must gain clarity. I am talking about using as much detail as you can imagine from the small sounds, colors, smells, and tastes and what it feels like to have already accomplished your intention.

Clarity sends your brain and the universe a specific (crystal-clear) message. When there is clarity, there is power. Ambiguity lends to confusion, and too much confusion slows down the creative process.

Write Ideal Life Screenplay

Your ideal life screenplay is exactly what it sounds like: a proposed screenplay or script that describes details of your ideal life. Create a picture on the screen of your mind of your ideal life. This is a process, and your picture will evolve over time. To start, you may want to write a script like a screenplay, such as one an actor reads while practicing for a play or movie. Set the scene at the point of accomplishment. Describe what it is like *when you have achieved your goal*. Do this in the present tense—as if it is happening right now.

Ask yourself some good, probing questions to help in this process. How do you want your story to unfold? What role are you playing? Who are the people around you? Who is congratulating you? Who is standing next to you? What are people saying to you? Where are you living? What do you smell? What sounds do you hear? What do you see around you? What are you wearing? What are you doing? How do you feel?

You are writing a movie, only this is the movie of your life, a true story that is about to happen. Start by fantasizing about your ideal life. See in your mind's eye your ideal life as if you were designing it the way you want it. This project may take some time to get all the details down. Get them down. In a movie script or screenplay, you have the characters, different scenes, and a variety of props. Get your journal out and have fun!

To guide you, write your script of your ideal scenario for each of the five major areas of your life: physical, mental, spiritual, financial, and relational. I'm assuming your primary focus when reading this book is the physical area. Therefore, we will be focusing on that first. Ultimately, I invite you to complete in full detail each area of your life as you would like it to be.

When you are mentally creating your ideal life, create your ideal body. Imagine every aspect of it. How do you look? How do you feel? What shape are you in? What are you wearing? What sizes are you wearing? Get as specific and precise as you can. If negative thoughts or emotions begin popping up, you may be getting too detailed—at least for now. Keep it positive. When you feel you have an accurate and complete vision, then write your vision on paper.

After you get your primary focus for the physical aspect of your new life, create an ideal scenario for the other areas of your life (mental, spiritual, financial, and relational). You will write scripts for each of these areas, but they will all blend together to form your ideal life. Each area is similar to scenes of a movie. They may be different, but they are all a part of the same movie. When you have completed a rough draft, read it and add any new ideas you think of. This new vision (your movie) will mature for a while. This is normal.

Assemble to Create Ideal Life Area Scripts

The ideal life area scripts are scripts of specific areas of your life, and when they are assembled together, they form the ideal life screenplay. Each life area might consist of one to ten or more pages. If you have followed the instructions above to write each specific area individually, then this step is complete. If you wrote them sporadically, gather all the details from each area and then separate them by each life area (physical, mental, financial, spiritual, and relational) to prepare for the next step.

DAY SIX

Check off these boxes as you complete each task.

- ❑ Beliefs
  - ❑ Identifying current beliefs
  - ❑ Creating a target belief
  - ❑ Installing new beliefs

BELIEFS

Day six: Belief. This step has multiple parts and is an ongoing process. After the previous assignments, you have a clear target or a vision. Now, it is time to proceed to the three-part process regarding beliefs. Part one is *evaluating and checking your starting point as far as your current beliefs,* part two is *setting up a target belief,* and part three is *creating a strong belief via the mental reconditioning process* (days eight and nine) *in order to reinforce your decision to achieve your goal*. Part three is an ongoing part of the process.

- Where are you now? (present results)
- What beliefs do you need to have ingrained to get to your new target?
- Install new beliefs

Identifying Current Beliefs

Most of this work was done in your assignment on day one. Remember when you took physical inventory? Based on those data, determine what beliefs were *installed* and running to create those types of results. What did you have to believe to perform at that level? This exercise may require some deep thinking, but the benefits will far outweigh any effort you exert.

What beliefs were needed to exist in your mind to have created those past effects? I ask because, when you reprogram the mind with new beliefs, it will help to know what programming (beliefs) you are replacing.

Setting Up a Target Belief

Now you know what beliefs were running. You know which beliefs were responsible for the undesirable results of your past. It is now time to determine what beliefs *need to be* in place, so that you can create the results you do want in your life.

- What must you think and believe to be the person you are intending to become?
- What beliefs do you have about exercise?
- What beliefs do you own regarding nutrition?
- What beliefs do you possess about personal development?

In addition, ask yourself further questions that occur to you regarding other beliefs that a person with your ideal life would own. When you answer those questions, you are ready to begin creating your new beliefs.

Installing New Beliefs

Once you know what you want and which beliefs you are choosing to establish, you can begin creating and installing them. This step is critical if your desires are to have long-term results.

The reprogramming process is ongoing and requires time and effort. This task is difficult to complete in a day. However, for the purpose of today's assignment, once you read and understand the reconditioning process, you can check it off the list. There are four main parts, along with other support aspects:

- Affirmations, visualizations, meditations, and mental martial arts (ANTs elimination).
- The reprogramming process is coming, and a solid foundation must be laid first. Therefore, stay committed and keep up the great work.

DAY SEVEN

Check off these boxes as you complete each task.

- ❑ Checkup—week one in review
  - ❑ Personal responsibility—past, present, and future
  - ❑ Personal commitment to do whatever it takes
  - ❑ Ascertain your desire and complete SEEQ
  - ❑ Make a DECISION to achieve desire
  - ❑ CLARITY by writing your ideal life screenplay
  - ❑ BELIEFS—current and created future belief target
  - ❑ Review your progress
- ❑ Celebrate—begin daily habit

CHECKUP—WEEK ONE IN REVIEW

Congratulations! You have completed one week! You deserve to congratulate yourself and celebrate. Celebration is another facet of this entire process and we will go into it in more depth later, but note that it is important to celebrate all your successes along the way.

If you had some challenges this week, congratulations! You are already growing, whether or not you realize it. One point to reiterate here is for you to be easy on yourself. In everyday terms, don't beat yourself up. If you have dropped the ball in certain areas, then today is the day for you to pick it up. If you have really had a challenge, then feel free to start over at day one. As long as you keep moving forward and persisting, it doesn't really matter how long it takes. The self-improvement path will get easier.

Week one lays the foundation so that you can begin building your new life in week two, when you address and begin the reprogramming process. You must build the foundation before you start construction on your new life. If you have missed any assignments or are unclear about any concepts, now is the time to go back and reread each area in which you need clarification.

Today's assignment is to review what you have done up to this point. Check your work. Tweak it. If you have missed something, make sure to do it. Read the quick list below and confirm that you have completed all of the necessary tasks. Please do this now. Remember, **a decision is not whether to do something or not but a reflection of who you are.** Who are you? You are a genius and a magnificent being, and, through this process, you will REMEMBER these facts if you haven't absorbed them yet. Keep moving.

YOUR RESPONSIBILITY PAST, PRESENT, AND FUTURE

You MUST take personal responsibility for your successes as well as for your past failures. This means that you take responsibility for your thoughts, feelings, behaviors, actions, and habits. Furthermore, this means that *you are responsible for all of your results.*

PERSONAL COMMITMENT TO DO WHATEVER IT TAKES

Commit to put forth every effort to the accomplishment of your goal. Put your commitment in writing by signing the binding agreement of personal commitment. Buy a journal or notebook and record your body measurement data. Begin to fantasize about your new, ideal body and record your thoughts about your ideal body in your journal.

ASCERTAIN DESIRE AND COMPLETE SEEQ

What are your desires? One way to dig them up is to complete the self evaluation and exploration questionnaire.

MAKE DECISION TO ACHIEVE YOUR DESIRE

You make a decision to develop exactly what it is you choose to have as a part of your new life, your ideal life. What are the results you desire? In this new life, what does your ideal body look like? Begin the search for your ideal body photo. Look for photos of your ideal body in a variety of magazines and/or search the Internet.

GAIN CLARITY—WRITE IDEAL LIFE SCREENPLAY

Get clarity by creating your ideal life screenplay, and within that, create your ideal body image. How do you want your life to unfold? What does your ideal body look and feel like?

EXPOSE BELIEFS—CREATE FUTURE BELIEF AIM

Evaluate and check your current beliefs. Set up a target belief. Then, develop strong, new beliefs via the mental reconditioning process (coming soon).

Review Progress

Day seven is the day to review your work, to catch up on any loose ends, and to recommit to the process for another week. You can do it. Keep at it. The toughest week is behind you. This past week was the steepest part of the hill. Keep climbing. I am with you every step of the way. The view from the top is worth your effort, and you will really appreciate it.

CELEBRATE—BEGIN DAILY HABIT

Now, let's celebrate. Celebrating your efforts is now a part of your everyday life, beginning with day one. It is critical to celebrate now. Pat yourself on the back and reward yourself for your efforts. When a baby is learning to walk, we celebrate one simple, little step. At this point, YOU are learning to *walk*, so **celebrate each step and you will be more willing to take the risk required to move to the next step.** There is a good probability that the child will fall, and as she learns the reward of cheering, smiles, and laughter, she takes the next step. Eventually, she learns to walk. Gradually, she becomes better at walking and walks faster. Soon, she runs. It all begins with a single step.

No matter what your results are from this last week, celebrate! From now on, **celebrate your results**. If you don't like them, celebrate the fact that you are aware that they don't yet meet your desired expectations. Celebrate! You deserve it. Do this daily.

DAY EIGHT

Check off these boxes as you complete each task.

- ❑ Reprogramming process recap
- ❑ Reprogramming cornerstone 1, phase 1
- ❑ Create affirmation sheet
- ❑ Create area affirmation statements (from ideal life area script)

REPROGRAMMING PROCESS RECAP

Day eight: When you commit to this practice, you are ready for the reprogramming or retraining process. The reprogramming process will help overwrite the past non-producing convictions as well as beliefs that hinder empowerment and instead install new, more empowering beliefs, behaviors, and habits. It will also help install new programs to put your success on autopilot and establish positive habits for a lifetime. This reprogramming process involves the following:

Cornerstone 1	Affirmations
Cornerstone 2	Visualizations
Cornerstone 3	Meditations
Cornerstone 4	Mental martial arts (ANTs illumination and elimination)

These are four major cornerstones of this process, and they are all critical to your success. Each one of these four cornerstones helped me achieve the successes I now enjoy.

To keep your daily assignments manageable, I separated the four cornerstones into their components.

Cornerstone 1 Affirmations

Phase 1 Affirmation sheet

Phase 2 Daily intention card

Phase 3 Create audio affirmation statement

Phase 4 Journal

REPROGRAMMING CORNERSTONE 1, PHASE 1

Cornerstone one is affirmations, and phase one is to create an affirmation sheet. Under the affirmations section, your action plan assignment is to **create your own personal affirmations**. We will be designing an affirmation sheet as well as a set of affirmations for each area of your life: physical, mental, spiritual, financial, and relational, to be known as the area affirmation statements.

Create Area Affirmation Statements

Review your ideal life screenplay (day five). Once you have a good self movie or ideal life screenplay and you are happy with the story for each area (ideal life area script), condense the story or script for each life area into one paragraph. These should be the most important sentences or statements you choose for your ideal life. Choose five to fifteen sentences that reflect your ideal life in each of the five major areas. These become your area affirmation statements. All five area statements will form your affirmation sheet.

For example, in my case, I can read aloud each area affirmation statement in one minute or less. There are approximately 120–180 words per area of life. Get as many details down as you can, while keeping it brief.

When you are done with this activity, you will have a more condensed version of your ideal life area scripts, called area affirmation statements. Take ten to fifteen minutes each day for several weeks and tweak your area affirmation statements. Get them as precise as you can. Work on your area affirmation statements until they resonate with you. We are not looking for perfection here, merely statements that excite you.

Three important points to follow: 1) state everything in a positive way, 2) use the present tense format, and 3) the details of your ideal body must be consistent with your ideal body photo. The photo, screenplay, scripts, and statements must describe your ideal body accurately and consistently. If the photo you have chosen is *not* ideal, then you need to find one that reflects the ideal body you intend to create.

Take the time now to create your affirmation sheet. For a sample sheet, visit www.donstaley.com/fitmindbook.

Create (Ideal Life) Affirmation Sheet

You now have five area affirmation statements—one for each of the five major areas of your life. When all five areas are put on one sheet of paper in *affirmation form*, I call this an ideal life affirmation sheet or affirmation sheet. *Affirmation form* means that it is stated in a positive way and in the present tense. This is an optimal format for programming the subconscious mind.

This sheet can include all areas of your life, and it must include your ideal health and fitness scenario—your ideal body statement.

Once you get all of this information on paper, tweak it so that it reads and flows well. After going over it a few times, it should roll off your tongue like a well-memorized song. Take your time tweaking your affirmation sheet because you will spend a lot of time with it, it is important that you are comfortable with it, and it needs to reflect your desires.

The perfect length of the affirmation sheet will vary from person to person. In printed form, mine is about one 8½" x 11" page and single spaced. I suggest that you avoid anything longer.

Read your affirmation sheet two to three times a day and, preferably, in front of the mirror. Reading in front of a mirror uses multiple senses and sends a stronger message to the brain, enhancing those neural connections.

The affirmation sheet is equivalent to putting the daily intention card on steroids. It covers the five major areas of your life: spiritual, mental, physical, financial, and relational.

> "An affirmation opens the door. It's a beginning point on the path to change."
>
> **—Louise L. Hay**

> "Any thought that is passed on to the subconscious often enough and convincingly enough is finally accepted."
>
> **—Robert Collier**

DAY NINE

Check off these boxes as you complete each task.

- ❑ Begin the reprogramming process cornerstone one, phase two
  - ❑ Condense to create ideal body affirmation
  - ❑ Create daily affirmations
  - ❑ Create daily intention card
  - ❑ Begin daily intention card habit

REPROGRAMMING, CORNERSTONE 1, PHASE 2

Day nine: Most of the first step in today's assignment is already complete because, in a previous assignment, you have already created your physical area affirmation statement, which encompasses your ideal body affirmation. The ideal body affirmation is one of the main parts of creating the daily affirmation. Add the ideal body affirmation together with one or two new beliefs and you have your daily affirmations.

Condense to Form Ideal Body Affirmation

When you finish your affirmation sheet, pull from that your main assertions or top intention statements for your physical area of life, or simply reduce your area affirmation statements down to about one to five sentences. This is your main objective. What is the statement that sums up your script or area affirmation statement for your physical area of your ideal life? This abbreviated statement does not include many of the minor details, and, ideally, it still generates significant feelings when you read it. Your intention statement will also be in the *affirmative form*. This smaller, more focused statement is your ideal body affirmation.

Create Daily Affirmations

Create an affirmation in line with your vision. You will write this affirmation on the daily intention card every day. Your affirmation should include your goal or intended target, ideal body affirmation, and an action or two that you must take every day to achieve your target.

In my case, there were a few main actions I intended to incorporate into my life: exercise every day, eat healthful foods, and drink plenty of water. Do you see the difference? I had my vision or goal (weigh 195 lb.), and I had an action or two that were necessary to accomplish the goal (exercise every day, eat healthful foods, and drink plenty of water).

The action is the behavior that is necessary to get you to your target. What action do you need to take every day to achieve your target?

Create a Daily Intention Card

Pick your *top intention statement*, which is your main area of focus (see mine in a few paragraphs). This book's main focus is <u>the physical area</u> to create an ideal body. However, in some cases, a person may use this book to focus on other areas of his or her life. Once you master the physical area, you may consider using this book again to focus on a different area of your life. Once you have selected your top statement, continue with the reconditioning process.

Now, reduce your affirmation statements to about one to five sentences, and make them the best flowing sentences you can arrange.

a) Take out a daily intention card (a 3" x 4" index card or any size you like) to carry in your pocket every day. At the top of the card, write the statement: "I am so happy and grateful now that...." Then, write your top statement on this card. As you write or read it, feel the *feelings* of joy and appreciation. Get excited! My card read similar to this:

"I am so happy and grateful now that I exercise every day. I weigh 190 pounds, with a 32-inch waist, and I have rock-hard, "six-pack" abs. I have a lean and muscular body with less than 9% body fat. I eat healthy foods and drink plenty of water. I have an abundance of physical and mental energy, and I feel and look great. I am as healthy as I've ever been."

Notice how it is all focused on one topic. At the time, this was my top intention statement. The length is one to five sentences, and it is very clear and measurable for the action I am taking (I exercise every day). Admittedly, it took some time to develop this refined statement. It doesn't happen in one day. At least in my case it didn't. It will take some tweaking and fine-tuning to get it down to one to five sentences. It was a process, and it took many attempts to get it exactly right for me. Be patient with yourself and have fun with the process.

b) In the early stages of the reprogramming process, write a statement that will "program" the reconditioning process. You may choose something like this:

"I devote ten to fifteen minutes (insert your minimum commitment time) every day to reprogram myself. I write my daily intention card every day, I carry it with me wherever I go, and I pull it out and read it several times a day—every day."

Keep this card with you always, and pull it out frequently to read it several times a day. Read it, feel it, and believe it. Your assignment is to do this exercise every day for thirty days. Actually, we will do this for 180 days, but let's begin with thirty. If you miss a day, start counting over from day one. Do it every day. Make this commitment now! You can get a sample, blank daily intention card by visiting www.donstaley.com/fitmindbook.

Do this activity for thirty days and be aware of the difference you feel about your new goal. In the beginning, choose to start with a simple goal card, as I did. Your affirmations are on one side with a picture of your main goal in the background, and perhaps the daily tasks you want to accomplish are on the other side. For example:

What I did to accomplish having a subtle image in the background of my affirmations required some ingenuity. First, I found an image I wanted. Then, I printed it on card stock, so the images printed the size of a card. Therefore, on one sheet, it printed nine to twelve images properly spaced. Then, using Microsoft Word, I created a document with the text copy of my affirmations and laid them out to match the location of the images. This took a few attempts. Once you line them up, you can then print several sheets. Finally, cut your affirmation cards out of the sheets.

Start your day by writing on this card. Ideally, this would be during a private time without distractions. It is important to set aside a few minutes of uninterrupted time to get this done, so awaken earlier to spend a few minutes by yourself. Thinking alone in the morning may be a new idea. If you are not already waking early and spending private time by yourself, then you must form a new habit. Decide to commit to this concept of *spending private time to write on your goal card* and incorporate the reconditioning process to speed up your progress.

Begin Daily Intention Card Habit

Today, begin writing your affirmations down on your daily intention card. Do it now as you read this, but starting tomorrow, do it the first thing in the morning, before you start your day. You can use a simple 3" x 5" card. Find what works for you and use it every day.

The daily intention card has multiple uses, and *affirmations* is just one such use. You can also find it in the section on visualizations and accountability. It is a good idea to refresh by taking a few minutes to reread those ideas now.

At this point, you are ready to continue with the next step in the reprogramming process.

DAY TEN

Check off these boxes as you complete each task.

- ❑ Accountability part one
  - ❑ Select your accountability partners
  - ❑ Select accountability and commitment agreement
    - ❑ Pick #1 or #2 or customize
  - ❑ Sign and send it to five accountability partners
  - ❑ Keep a copy for yourself and send an email version to me

ACCOUNTABILITY PART ONE

Day ten: Today, you begin part one of the accountability process. There are four main parts of the accountability process, and it begins with the signing and sending of the accountability and commitment agreement.

Select Your Accountability Partners

Think of several people who could help keep you accountable. When you have a list, put them into two categories. The first category is "tough love." The second category includes those individuals you feel would show you unconditional love.

Choose three people to help you who fall into the "tough love" category. Then, pick two different people who fit the category of "unconditional love." This gives you five people who will be your accountability buddies. Each of the five individuals you choose will get a signed copy of your accountability and commitment agreement. Plus, as a rite of passage, send one to me via email to don@donstaley.com with the subject heading of "Rite of Passage." Sending this e-mail to me signifies your commitment to achieve your goal(s) and is the beginning of your journey toward the accomplishment of your intentions.

SELECT YOUR AGREEMENT

On upcoming pages are two different commitment agreements. The first is specifically a fitness agreement. The second is a general agreement that can be used for any goal. Pick the one that is best suited for your particular objective. If neither of these two agreements resonates with you, then feel free to create your own agreement. However, you must follow the following instructions.

If you decide to send a customized agreement, then begin tweaking the agreement at once. You must maintain certain aspects of the agreement, which include the following:

- Commit for the next sixty to ninety days, every day
- Commit to the reprogramming process
- Commit to take daily action toward your goal
- Commit to a penalty if you do not take action
- Commit to a reward when you do take action

Pick the First Commitment Agreement or the Second, or Customize

Customize your commitment agreement exactly the way you want it. If you are not able to complete your customized agreement within an hour, then please complete the original commitment agreement provided and state that you will send a revised, customized agreement within three days. This will give you time to create your own. However, you will still be held accountable for your actions—or lack of actions—in the interim. It is critical that you use one of the agreements provided or create a customized agreement *right now*. Have it completed within an hour and mail or email it. Do it now!

SIGN AND SEND ACCOUNTABILITY AND COMMITMENT AGREEMENT TO FIVE PARTNERS

You have already committed yourself to your goal and to the process when you completed day two's assignments. Now you are going to commit to the specific steps necessary for the accomplishment of the goal; you will then share this commitment with others who can help.

When you commit to this process, you will read this book a minimum of three times. If you are not committed, *your resolve will be shaken* at the first sign of trouble. Decide to commit to this process because you deserve it. To keep on track, employ the help of people you trust to hold you accountable.

A commitment agreement is essentially a contract with yourself. You are making a pledge to take certain actions to move you toward your goals. This agreement holds you accountable because:

1. You are putting your intentions in writing.
2. You are sending your written intentions to several people who will keep you on track.
3. You are specifying *rewards* and *punishments* for your actions and inactions.

The accountability and commitment agreement is a huge step in moving you to action. There are two motivational principles at work here. The first is your moving away from pain and the second is your moving toward pleasure. These are the two biggest motivators in human psychology.

Most people will do more to avoid pain than they will to seek pleasure. On the other hand, there are some who would rather move toward pleasure than avoid pain. In this agreement, we are using both motivators, so no matter which mode works best for you, we have covered all the bases. When you get the agreements completed, you will email or send them by regular mail to the five people on your list.

Keep a Copy for You and Send an Email Version to Me

Next, send an email version of this agreement to me. You will need seven contracts altogether. You'll keep the seventh copy for yourself. Photocopy the accountability and commitment agreement page (I give you permission). Print one copy for yourself, sign it, and keep it where you will see it every day.

Pick one agreement and use it. You can visit www.donstaley.com/fitmindbook for a free PDF version of each of the agreements.

"If you want to know your past—look into your present conditions. If you want to know your future—look into your present actions."

—Chinese proverb

Accountability and Commitment

Agreement #1 (FITNESS)

On this ___________day of ____________in the year 20____, I, __________________, do enter into this contract willingly and with full knowledge of what is expected of me by me. I enter into this contract to commit myself to being physically fit by creating permanent fitness habits through reconditioning my mind with the reprogramming process.

My plan of action is this:

I reserve a minimum of 30–60 minutes*, seven days a week during the next 90 days for the mental reprogramming (retraining) process.

1. I follow the coaching program laid out by Don Staley in his book *FIT MIND, FIT BODY.*
2. I follow all action steps in the 30-day action plan in the book *FIT MIND, FIT BODY,* including the four parts of the reprogramming process.
3. I take action on a daily basis with my action goals to accomplish my target of____
4. On a daily basis, I reward myself for my successful efforts with:
   ____
5. On a weekly basis, I reward myself for my successful efforts with:
   ____
6. When I have accomplished my objective of ________________________, I shall take my family _____________ (insert your preference [picnic, camping, vacation, etc.]) and spend a day or two relaxing—complete with a picnic lunch of my favorite foods. I will take pictures, rejoice in my favorite picnic place and celebrate my success.
7. By doing these things, I plan to have reached my ideal weight of __________ by ____Day, ______Month, 20__.
8. By ____Day, ______Month, 20__, I will begin phase two of my fitness program.

I realize the importance of each person to whom I have sent a copy of this contract, and I call on each one to police my heartfelt efforts in whatever loving way he or she chooses. If I am caught falling behind on any of the goals listed above and their corresponding deadlines, I hereby promise to treat the detector—that person who receives an official copy of this contract—to a dinner at his or her favorite restaurant.

________________________________ ____________________

Signed Date

*In the beginning it may be 10–15 minutes.

Email/mail five copies to your accountability partners. Email one copy to me at: don@donstaley.com. Print, sign, and keep a copy for yourself.

See appendix 5 for agreement #2

DAY ELEVEN

Check off these boxes as you complete each task.

- ❑ Accountability part two
  - ❑ Daily journal—begin habit
  - ❑ Daily calendar
  - ❑ Daily card
- ❑ Create other habits

ACCOUNTABILITY PART TWO

Day eleven: Most successful people didn't get there by themselves. I didn't accomplish what I did by myself either. Acquire the wisdom, expertise, and help of others if you are serious about achieving your goals. A good practice for keeping yourself accountable is to enlist the help of others (days ten and twenty-six), as well as doing it yourself (day eleven).

You can acquire external help in two primary methods: 1) individually, such as through a friend, coach, or mentor and 2) as part of a group, such as a mastermind group. Both of these methods will be a later assignment (day twenty-six). Also, you must keep yourself accountable. Certain tools, such as a daily journal, calendar, and a daily card, can help keep you accountable.

Begin Habit of Writing Daily Journal

You make yourself accountable by recording your daily accomplishments so that you can see your progress—or lack of it—as a reminder to verify that you have done your tasks for the day. If you have been using a journal as assigned, you are on the right track.

Now, it is time to use your journal for accountability also. You can do this by simply writing a small summary of each day's accomplishments and challenges. This action serves as a reference—not as something with which to "beat yourself up." Notice patterns and habits. Remember, most of your actions and behaviors are habits, and ultimately, these accountability exercises are done to modify your habits to help you accomplish your goal.

Calendar—Daily

Get a calendar that you can readily see. I used a big, three-foot by four-foot laminated wall calendar, which I placed prominently on my office wall. Use whatever works. A calendar's main purpose is to serve as a reminder. It can also display your accomplishments daily—if you did what you intended to do for the day. I suggest that it be a physical calendar that you can place on your desk, wall, or nightstand. If it is on your computer and you don't look at your computer one day, you could miss being reminded.

After you do your main tasks for the day, you can color in that day, box it in, or add a prominent check mark. In some fashion, indicate that you have accomplished the task(s) for the day. Develop the habit of checking your calendar before going to sleep every day, as a reminder that you have accomplished what you intended to do that day. If you have missed something, do it right then.

Daily Card

As you know by now, the daily card is a multiple-purpose tool. In this section, we are using it as an accountability tool. At the end of the day, you can verify the completion of—or not having completed—the daily tasks and rituals that you have committed to doing each day. If they are not checked off by the end of the day, it is time to get them completed.

This card serves as a reminder similar to the calendar, but because you carry it with you wherever you go, it helps when you are out of town or away from home. Incorporate the habit of using this card, and it will assist you in the accomplishment of your goals.

CREATE OTHER NEW HABITS

The following is a list of some other potential habits to acquire along the way to help facilitate and implement the mental reconditioning process. The more of these you make into habits, the faster you will see results.

- Awaken earlier. Ten to fifteen minutes is a minimum.
- Upon waking, say to yourself, "Thank you," and be grateful for the new day and opportunities in store.
- Pick up your card and read it.
- Every morning, go to your quiet place and write a new daily card for the day.
- Carry your daily intention card with you everywhere.
- Touch, look at, and read the card frequently during the day.
- Visualize and be sensitive to feelings of accomplishment as you read the card.
- Put your card by your bed so that it is the last thing you see before you sleep and the first thing you see in the morning.
- Read the card just before you go to sleep.
- Read the affirmation sheet aloud in front of a mirror one to three times a day.

The next day, the process begins again. These rituals need to be "practiced" every day, *with no exceptions*. You do not need to take them all on at once, but you must do these things every day for at least thirty days, and then for an additional ninety days—for a minimum of 120 days. Most likely, you will choose to continue performing this process for the remainder of your life. It is that powerful.

DAY TWELVE

Check off these boxes as you complete each task.

- ❑ Visualization, cornerstone two
    - ❑ Ideal body photo: decide on initial ideal body photo
    - ❑ Copy and post in car, bathroom, office, etc.

VISUALIZATION, CORNERSTONE 2

Day twelve: Your next assignment is to prepare for visualization by finding an ideal body photo. You began this search on day four and now is the time to finalize this search—at least for now—and choose your ideal photo.

Decide on Initial Ideal Body Photo

Searching for images or photos online could easily render you a million possibilities, with one being close to, if not exactly, the body you choose to create for yourself. The photo or image must resonate with you. This body image may evolve as you progress. For now, choose one. Get started. Ideally, you will pick a photo of someone who has the same physical bone structure and approximate height as you. Get as precise as you can. Make sure the photo matches your ideal body. Beware of the crippling tendency to let perfectionism get in the way of progress. *Good enough* is better than not getting it done!

Copy and Post

You may want to be selective about where you post your ideal body images until you have completed thirty to sixty days of reconditioning. At that point, you can probably post your ideal body photo everywhere. I say this because you may live with others or have visitors who may see this new image of you. When they do, and if the "new" body image is significantly different from your current body, chances are good that they may make a negative comment or even laugh. Most likely, they won't realize that you are stretching yourself and striving for a very different ideal body. Such a potential negative response could be discouraging, and we want to control this environment until you reach a point when you can handle that type of feedback.

Some people will attempt to shoot down your dreams because they may believe subconsciously that if you are doing well, it makes them look bad. After you have been reconditioned, it won't matter as much because comments like that will have little or no effect. It is wise to be prepared for some derogatory comments or gestures. However, if you can honestly say that hearing people make negative comments or laughing about your new image won't bother you, or if you have thick skin, then go for it. Initially, put your ideal body photos where only you can see them, and as you grow in confidence and conditioning, you can put them everywhere.

Make copies of your ideal body image and place them where you can see them frequently. Place one on the front (or back) side of your affirmation sheet. Other locations to consider are your bedroom, bathroom, office, car, and kitchen. Do this now!

DAY THIRTEEN

Check off these boxes as you complete each task.

- ❑ Create vision board
- ❑ Finalize ideal body photo

VISION BOARD

Day thirteen: Your next assignment is to create a vision board, which represents everything you desire in all areas of your life—physical, mental, spiritual, financial, and in your relationships (relational). You can arrange your vision board any way you choose. I have mine arranged in those areas on three different vision boards. My vision boards are arranged with things I choose to be, to do, and to have. I have one vision board as my "accomplished" board. When you use your imagination, the possibilities for vision boards are unlimited. The important thing is that you feel good when you look at any one of your vision boards.

You can find images or photos online at websites such as Google, Flickr, MySpace, Facebook, and other free sites. An example of an additional, paid site is istockphoto.com. A simple Internet search for images or photos should net you numerous options. Find the perfect image for you.

Magazines are also a great source for photos. You may want to digitize any actual photos or pictures by scanning the images to a file. If you don't know how to do this, then take them to an office supply store or a copying store and they can scan the images to a digital file for a small charge.

You do want a digital file so that you can place your photos on your *digital* vision board. This can exist on any digital device you may own, such as a video MP3 player, mobile phone, or computer. Post your ideal image to any electronic devices you have, and if you don't have any, you might consider investing in your reconditioning by making a purchase. **The idea is to bombard yourself with these positive images.** Add your face to as many of the photos as you can to customize them so that *YOU* appear being, doing, and having whatever is in the photos.

This process takes some time and is well worth the effort. This process is an evolution. Be on the lookout for photos that inspire you. When you find images that move you, add them to your vision board.

FINALIZE IDEAL BODY PHOTO

It is now time to *finalize* your ideal body photo. This doesn't mean you won't change it later, but for now, it is what you will work with until you encounter a photo which inspires you to update it. If you do alter your ideal body photo, then to complete this assignment you are expected to update *all* of your ideal body photos. If you have already committed to your pervious ideal body photo, then you are finished for today. Good work.

"Your imagination is your preview of life's coming attractions."

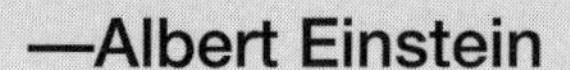

DAY FOURTEEN

Check off these boxes as you complete each task.

- ❑ Checkup—week two in review
  - ❑ Began celebrating
  - ❑ Create area affirmations
  - ❑ Create affirmation statement
  - ❑ Create daily affirmations
  - ❑ Begin habit of writing daily affirmations
  - ❑ Sign and send accountability & commit agreement
  - ❑ Begin writing daily journal habit
  - ❑ Ideal body photo search and selection continues
  - ❑ Post ideal body photo prominently
  - ❑ Create vision boards
  - ❑ Finalize ideal body photo and update
- ❑ Awareness

CHECKUP WEEK TWO IN REVIEW

Day fourteen: Congratulations, you have made it through two weeks! You deserve to congratulate yourself and celebrate. You are building momentum. Week two was intense, and your work load will lighten in week three, so be sure to keep your commitment going. Persist, persist, persist! Let's review your efforts for week two.

BEGIN CELEBRATING

During last week's review, you began to implement celebration into your life. Celebrate regardless of your results from this past week! From now on, celebrate your results. Remember, if you don't like your results, celebrate that you are aware enough to realize that fact. **You need *awareness* to find what you like.** Celebrate everything daily. You deserve it.

Create Area Affirmations

Condense your ideal life area statements into the most important five to fifteen sentences or statements. These should reflect your ideal life in each of the five major life areas.

Create Affirmation Statement

All five area statements compiled on one page form your *affirmation sheet.*

Create Daily Affirmations

Create an affirmation in line with your vision. Rewrite this affirmation on the daily intention card every day. Your affirmation is to include your intended target. The ideal body affirmation is a task and reprogramming action(s) you must take every day to achieve your target.

Begin Habit of Writing Daily Affirmations

Begin writing your affirmations the first thing in the morning on your daily intention card. Do this every day. Write them before you start your day. A simple 2½" x 4" or 3" x 5" card works very well.

Sign and Send Accountability & Commit Agreement

Select five accountability partners. Select an agreement or create a customized agreement, sign it, and send it to each partner. Keep one copy for yourself, and email one to me as a rite of passage.

Begin Habit of Writing in Daily Journal

Every day, write a small summary of that day's accomplishments and challenges in your journal. Make this activity a habit. Persist, and it will become a habit.

Ideal Body Photo Search and Selection

Find and select an ideal body photo. You began this search on day four and now is the time to pick one to work with. Choose your ideal photo immediately.

Post Ideal Body Photo Prominently

Post your ideal body photo where you can see it several times a day.

Create Vision Boards

Produce a vision board with everything you intend to create in all five areas of your life—which are physical, mental, spiritual, financial, and in your relationships (relational).

Finalize Ideal Body Photo and Update

Finalize your ideal body photo. Pick and commit to your ideal body photo. If you change this photo, you must update it wherever it is posted.

AWARENESS PHASE 1

As you progress through this book, many ideas are meant for everyday practice and eventually to become daily habits. You will use some ideas only occasionally. In some fashion, they will all become a regular part of your life, whether or not you use them daily. One such idea is to be more aware. The practice of gratitude (which is assigned in next week's review) will automatically force you to be more aware of your surroundings.

Being aware improves your life. Perhaps everything has been black and white. With more awareness, you can see in color. I remember as a child when we finally got a color TV. The difference was amazing. Now, technology has brought us LCD and plasma screen TVs, and you can see a tick at fifty yards. Who knows what is next? When you become more aware, more of the finer details of life begin to show up and you will be more prepared for opportunities, and that helps you paint your masterpiece life painting.

Being cognizant of your outside environment is of great value, but it is also important to be aware of your internal thoughts. Accordingly, you will be using your journal to keep tabs on your automatic negative thoughts (ANTs) in the upcoming week's assignments.

Keep a dossier on yourself. Make your journal your friend and track your own thoughts, feelings, and behaviors. What thoughts, feelings, and behaviors are in harmony with your new intentions, and which ones need to be upgraded? **When you write down your thoughts, you become even more aware.** Be sure to write them down. You don't have to keep a written dossier on yourself 24/7/365, but do make it a regular daily habit to keep aware of your thoughts.

Awareness isn't just tracking thoughts and events in your journal. **Being *aware* is being in the moment.** There is always something going on. Use all of your senses to experience life, and also be aware that there is always more going on.

DAY FIFTEEN

Check off these boxes as you complete each task.

- ❑ Begin meditation practice, cornerstone three

MEDITATION, CORNERSTONE 3

Day fifteen: Meditation is a very important part of this self-improvement process, and the sooner you can include it in your program, the faster it will help you reach your goals. As a part of our home study and coaching program, we have a meditation CD to help facilitate your efforts. I invite you to join the program, but if you are not a part of that program, you can do a simple breathing meditation. You will focus on your breath going in and out of your nose and release all thoughts as they come into your mind. Initially, start with five to ten minutes.

Think of beginning a meditation program as if you were starting a weight-lifting program. You don't jump into using the big weights until you have warmed up or until you are conditioned and your muscles are able to lift those heavy weights. The same approach is true for meditation. You want to **begin slowly and extend your time as you progress through the process**. You are building a muscle, albeit a mental and spiritual muscle.

If you have any questions, you can refer to chapter 12 on reconditioning. Look in the meditation section for detailed instructions. As a quick recap, simply get into a space where you won't be disturbed and sit in a comfortable chair. Next, get into a relaxed state, take a few deep breaths in through your nose, and let them out through your mouth. Then begin to focus on breathing in and out of your nose. When a thought enters your mind, simply release it and focus back on your breath. This endeavor takes practice, especially if you are new to meditation. As with any new skill you are learning, it takes a certain amount of repetition before you become proficient at it. Please be patient with yourself and remember to have fun.

DAY SIXTEEN

Check off these boxes as you complete each task.

- ❑ Mental martial arts process, cornerstone four—day one
  - ❑ Become aware of your ANTs (automatic negative thoughts)
  - ❑ Record ANTs in journal
  - ❑ Perform mental martial arts on your ANTs
  - ❑ Create a counteractive reply

Mental Martial Arts, Cornerstone 4

Next, you will begin to apply the principles and techniques to control and redirect your automatic negative thoughts. You will perform mental martial arts on your ANTs.

Become Aware of Your ANTs

Pay attention to your internal dialogue. Become more aware of your thoughts, especially negative thoughts. You can perform the next step only when you are cognizant of your automatic negative thoughts. Alert yourself whenever you speak or think a negative thought.

One method to make you more aware of those automatic negative thoughts is to create a daily journal and record your automatic negative thoughts.

Record ANTs in Journal

This week, take five days, including at least one day of your weekend, and record your ANTs in your daily journal. The idea is to get a sample from both your working or school time and your free time or non-working time. If you don't already have a journal (see day one), I recommend that you buy one right now. It doesn't have to be fancy; a simple spiral notebook works fine. Plan on carrying it around in public for a few days.

If carrying a journal in public is a new habit for you, it may be uncomfortable. It is perfectly normal to feel uncomfortable when you are doing something new, so feel it, recognize it, embrace it, and realize that what is happening is your amygdala seeking homeostasis.

When you notice a level of discomfort, you can celebrate the fact that you are making progress as a result of your increased awareness. In the past, you may have felt feelings of uneasiness, which might have pushed you back into your comfort zone without your realizing what was happening. The objective is for you to be aware when you experience these feelings (chemicals rushing through your body), to understand that this is normal, and to keep taking action toward your goal as long as you are safe. Remember that we celebrate both successes and failures.

When you get your journal, keep track of your negative thoughts by writing them down. Examples of some negative thoughts might be:

- "This stuff doesn't work."
- "I have failed for so long. Why would this work now?"
- "I'm just going to go back to my old habits."
- "Old dogs can't learn new tricks."
- "This is too difficult."
- "I hate this."
- "Why does this have to be so hard?"
- "I'm not good enough."
- "I'm not worthy."

Whatever your thoughts are, if they are negative, I want you to capture them in your journal. This activity helps in two ways. First, it is critical in the devaluing of that thought, because now you made it more tangible—you can see it on paper. Secondly*, it will help you be aware of what is* *happening in your mind! When those automatic negative thoughts (ANTs) occur, stomp them out*!

For the beginning of the ANTs extermination process, *carry* your *journal for five days to a week. Creating a solid habit* will most likely require your conscious awareness over the next 90–180 days. If, after five to seven days, you choose to continue to carry the journal to capture your ANTs, feel free to do so. Otherwise, the most important part is simply being aware of your thoughts and "handling" them on an ongoing basis. As a candidate for the automatic negative thought extermination process presents itself, apply the mental martial arts technique to eliminate it. This is a task that is critical to create into a permanent habit.

Perform Mental Martial Arts on Your Automatic Negative Thoughts (ANTs)

Whenever you are "attacked" by ANTs, simply acknowledge them with gratitude and redirect them into a new, more empowering thought by replacing them with a new thought and idea you are now creating in your ideal life. For example, "Thank you for serving me in the past. I no longer need you. I now choose this [replace with your new thought]."

Create a Counteractive Reply

My internal dialogue to replace health and fitness ANTs goes something like this:

> "Thank you for serving me in the past.
> I no longer need you. I NOW choose to be
> perfectly healthy and fit."

Take a moment and create a reply or rebuttal to the automatic negative thoughts that may pop up. Remember the Boy Scouts' motto? Be prepared! I am prepared for those nasty ANTs. You must prepare as well. It takes only a few minutes, but you will be armed to defeat automatic negative thoughts when you have prepared counteractive replies.

For every target (goal) you choose to have in your life, there are certain thoughts, actions, behaviors, and habits that must take place for you to accomplish that objective. Keep your thoughts positive and in alignment with your intentions.

As you progress, you will experience fewer and fewer ANTs. Once you embrace this process, you may be subject to occasional automatic negative thoughts, but from my experience, they will be very limited and will rarely occur. Whenever you start something new, or take your "game" (whatever that is) to a higher playing field (upping your game), another level of ANTs may present themselves. Now you know how to eliminate them, so, whatever your new goal may be, it will be easier to accomplish because of your new level of awareness and understanding. As you progress, you will have fewer ANTs. Therefore, when they do show up, they will be easier to recognize.

For the next four days, days seventeen through twenty, you will reread and repeat the assignments for day sixteen. Become aware of your ANTs, perform mental martial arts on your ANTs, record any ANTs in your journal, and use the reply or rebuttal for your ANTs you created on day sixteen. Reread and repeat day sixteen, except that there is no need to create another rebuttal.

DAY SEVENTEEN

Check off these boxes as you complete each task.

- ❑ Mental martial arts process—day two
  - ❑ Reread day sixteen assignment
  - ❑ Become aware of your ANTs
  - ❑ Perform martial arts on your ANTs
  - ❑ Record ANTs in journal

DAY EIGHTEEN

Check off these boxes as you complete each task.

- ❑ Mental martial arts process—day three
  - ❑ Reread day sixteen
  - ❑ Become aware of your ANTs
  - ❑ Perform martial arts on your ANTs
  - ❑ Record ANTs in journal

DAY NINETEEN

Check off these boxes as you complete each task.

- ❑ Mental martial arts process—day four
  - ❑ Reread day sixteen
  - ❑ Become aware of your ANTs
  - ❑ Perform martial arts on your ANTs
  - ❑ Record ANTs in journal

DAY TWENTY

Check off these boxes as you complete each task.

- ❑ Mental martial arts process—day five
  - ❑ Reread day sixteen
  - ❑ Become aware of your ANTs
  - ❑ Perform martial arts on your ANTs
  - ❑ Record ANTs in journal

This wraps up the major aspects, or the four cornerstones, of the actual mental reconditioning process. Although this entire book concerns habit formation or the reconditioning process, the four cornerstones of affirmations, visualizations, meditations, and the mental martial arts process of ANTs illumination and elimination are the most critical. As we finish this week, we will incorporate some gratitude.

DAY TWENTY-ONE

Check off these boxes as you complete each task.

- ❑ Checkup—week three in review
  - ❑ Begin awareness phase one
  - ❑ Begin meditation practice
  - ❑ Become aware of your ANTs
  - ❑ Record ANTs in journal
  - ❑ Perform martial arts on your ANTs
  - ❑ Create a counter reply
- ❑ Gratitude

CHECKUP WEEK THREE IN REVIEW

Day twenty-one: Congratulations, you have completed three weeks! With each step, you are getting mentally and spiritually stronger. Keep putting one foot in front of other, and in a short while, you can look back and wonder, "How did I get here?" Let's review your efforts for week three.

Begin Awareness Phase 1

Awareness isn't just tracking thoughts and events in your journal. *Being aware is being in the moment.* There is always something going on. Use all of your senses to experience life. As much as you can, take a few moments to soak it all in. Listen. Really listen. See things you might not normally notice. Smell whatever is there. Feel the texture of things. Use all your senses.

Begin Meditation Practice

Do a simple breathing meditation, in which you focus on your breath going in and out of your nose. When a thought enters your mind—and it will—

simply release it and concentrate on your breath. Initially, start with five to ten minutes and meditate every day.

Become aware of your automatic negative thoughts (ANTs). Pay attention to your internal dialogue. Become more aware of your thoughts, especially your negative thoughts.

Record ANTs in Journal

This week, take five days—including at least one day of your weekend plus one day of your working week—and record your ANTs in your daily journal.

Perform Martial Arts on Your ANTs

Whenever you are "attacked" by ANTs, simply acknowledge them with gratitude and redirect them into a new, more empowering thought. Replace them with a new thought you choose to create in your ideal life.

Create a Counter Reply

So you can perform martial arts on your ANTs, create a "direction" where you will be throwing them. Take a moment and create a reply or rebuttal to the ANTs that may pop up. Be prepared for those nasty ANTs with a cunning rebuttal.

Repeat Process (for four additional days)

You have repeated this process (except for creating a counter reply) every day for five days in a row. This will alert all your ANTs that *you* are now in charge of this picnic and that their party is over, while yours is just beginning.

GRATITUDE

Your next action item is to express gratitude (see chapter 14). Every day, when you get out of bed in the morning and before your feet hit the floor, say and feel, "Thank you." After watching the film *The Secret* on DVD several times, I began to implement this notion of gratitude. It is a great way to start the day. What a wonderful message or vibration to send out to begin your day!

As a reminder from chapter 14, appreciation or gratitude is the vibration of love. What you send out, you get back. It is also a great idea to do this during your day. The more you feel and experience gratitude, the more you will enjoy life and the more good you will receive. Make a habit of being grateful. Remember the old saying, take time to stop and smell the flowers? If you stop and pay attention, there are "flowers" everywhere. Take notice. Done with deep sincerity, this idea of consistently practicing gratitude and making it a habit can make a tremendous difference in your life. If this is all you get from this book, it will improve your life. Put gratitude in your life and practice it every day!

DAY TWENTY-TWO

Check off these boxes as you complete each task.

- ❑ Increase meditation time duration
- ❑ Continue martial arts on ANTs
- ❑ Continue gratitude

INCREASE MEDITATION TIME DURATION

Day twenty-two: This is a good time to improve your meditation each day by increasing the time you spend doing it. If you were new to meditation, you started off with five to ten minutes daily to build your meditation muscle. Beginning today, it is necessary for you to increase your time to ten to fifteen minutes each day. Just as if you were lifting weights, to advance, you need to increase the weights as you get stronger.

Enjoy this relatively light day, but remember that you have all of your other daily routines that you are incorporating from previous chapters, such as mental martial arts and gratitude.

DAY TWENTY-THREE

Check off these boxes as you complete each task.

- ❑ ANTs review
- ❑ Journal on five-day ANTs experience
- ❑ Continue martial arts on ANTs
- ❑ Continue gratitude

ANTs REVIEW

Day twenty-three: Review the thoughts and feelings experienced last week while working with your automatic negative thoughts. Did you experience any negative thoughts? Were you aware of any? Was there a particular thought that continued to pop up? Did a particular thought occur more frequently than others? What did you learn from this process? How did *noticing* these thoughts impact the way you felt? Were you able to stomp out the ANTs? Did you experience progress?

JOURNAL ON FIVE-DAY ANTs EXPERIENCE

Take your thoughts and answers to the preceding questions and write them down in your journal. Write about this experience and capture any thoughts, feelings, and ideas you may have gleaned from this practice.

CONTINUE MARTIAL ARTS ON ANTs

The five-day ANTs process was only the beginning of mastering your mind and controlling ANTs. Continue to stomp out any ANTs that occur by performing mental martial arts on them. However, you don't necessarily need to continue recording them in your journal. You can now do this process in your mind. If you again choose to use the journal for your ANTs sometime in the future, that is fine. However, it is not necessary any longer.

DAY TWENTY-FOUR

Check off these boxes as you complete each task.

- ❑ Create audio affirmations
- ❑ Begin listening to audio affirmations daily
- ❑ Continue martial arts on ANTs
- ❑ Continue gratitude (forever)

CREATE AUDIO AFFIRMATIONS

Day twenty-four: **Your next assignment is to create an audio version of your affirmation sheet.** Record yourself as you read your affirmation sheet aloud. With this recording, you will create an MP3 and/or audio CD. These are your audio affirmations. Your audio affirmations are about three to five minutes in length.

Ideally, you will record this in your own voice, one that you trust. **Get it done and get it done now.** If you are able to talk, I highly encourage you to use your voice. However, if you don't like your voice, get someone else to make the recording for you. This audio doesn't have to be of recording studio quality. In fact, a simple voice recorder works fine, as long as you have the ability to connect it to your computer, upload the file, and save it as an MP3 or similar file. **If you wait for perfection, you will never take action. The most important aspect of this entire chapter is to TAKE ACTION!**

"If you wait to do everything until you're sure it's right, you'll probably never do much of anything."

—Win Borden

To make things simpler, you can use iTunes or whatever other audio program is currently available. With all the latest programs and newest technologies, this activity keeps getting easier. If you have been conditioned to believe that you are not a techie or are less than savvy about recording, get a kid in your neighborhood to do it for you. Someone can help you.

Another thing I used was a CD player. I would play a CD of my audio affirmations all night while I slept. Sometimes, my wife would ask me to turn it down, and at times I actually wore headphones while I slept. However, those are not the most comfortable things to wear while sleeping. There may be companies that offer headphones that are comfortable to sleep in, but at the time, I had a normal pair of headphones and would occasionally use earbuds. In the morning, my ears would be sore.

Eventually, I reverted back to playing my audio affirmations aloud on my CD player and kept the volume down so my wife could sleep. Later, I bought an iPod-compatible alarm clock, so that I could connect my iPod. When my alarm went off, it was my affirmations that I heard. What a great way to awaken! Also, the clock had a timer, so I could play the iPod for a time before it shut off.

Now, I can play my affirmations for thirty, sixty, or ninety minutes as I go off to sleep, which is actually the best time to listen to them. This is the sweet spot in reconditioning. The states of grogginess just before you go to sleep or just as you are waking up are the best times to do this reconditioning process. If you are not able to hit the sweet spot exactly, it's fine to listen to your affirmations all night. I can also set this clock to alarm with a particular track on my iPod, so that I can wake to certain music or to my affirmations.

BEGIN LISTENING TO AUDIO AFFIRMATIONS DAILY

Now you have a written version and an audio version of your affirmations. I recommend listening to your audio affirmations a minimum of once a day, although three times would be great. Certainly, the more you listen, the better. Do remember to add feelings of accomplishment when you listen.

Once the audio is imported to iTunes, you can burn it to a CD or upload it to your MP3 player. The idea is to have your audio affirmations available in your car and on your MP3 player, mobile phone, and computer, so that you can listen several times a day—any time you want.

When I first began this process, I recorded my initial version, tweaked it and rerecorded it every month or two. I would listen to it and repeat the words aloud as I did my workout. When you create *your* audio affirmations, you can listen to your affirmation statements during whatever exercise you elect to do.

Because I wanted results as fast as possible, I used multiple methods or techniques to expedite the process. When I read my affirmation sheet, I listened to the audio as I read this statement and repeated it aloud. I was seeing the words, I was vocalizing the words (so my brain was processing the words to say), and I was hearing the words from my voice and from the recording in an interesting, stereo-type effect. This was a great way to triple-dip and get more bang for my buck. In my opinion, this method is much more effective than just reading affirmations.

As you progress through this process, you may choose to keep it fresh, exciting, and fun by varying how you do the affirmations and other reprogramming exercises. This process works so much faster when you are having fun!

DAY TWENTY-FIVE

Check off these boxes as you complete each task.

- ❑ Decide on final ideal body photo
- ❑ Copy and post
- ❑ Continue doing martial arts on ANTs

DECIDE ON FINAL IDEAL BODY PHOTO

Day twenty-five: After spending hours searching for images or photos, it is now time to finalize your ideal body photo. The photo or image must resonate with you. Stick with it for the next sixty, ninety, 180, or however many days, weeks, or months it takes. This image is your ideal body. If you are inspired with the ideal body photo, your assignment for today is simple.

COPY AND POST

You may have already selected and posted your final ideal body photo if you are sticking with your previous one. If that is the case, you can spend an extra ten minutes staring at your new ideal body and fantasizing about all the fun things you will experience when you achieve it. If not, it is time to knuckle down and find and DECIDE on your ideal body photo. **You must make a decision. If you have multiple ideal body targets, you will miss all of them**. PICK ONE NOW. Make a decision and commit to that decision. Avoid picking one you *think* you can achieve. **Pick the image you *choose to create* for your ideal body.** Of course, you can upgrade down the road. When you have made that final selection, then copy and post your ideal body photo everywhere.

DAY TWENTY-SIX

Check off these boxes as you complete each task.

- ❑ Accountability part three
- ❑ Find a coach. Begin your search

ACCOUNTABILITY PART 3

Day twenty-six: Keeping yourself accountable is wise and an integral part of success. It will be very advantageous to have help, because people have days when they are not at their best. This is the ebb and flow of life (the Law of Rhythm). If you know that someone is watching (figuratively), it will help you over some hurdles that you might neglect if you were doing all of these exercises by yourself. **It is time to begin the process of finding a talented coach.**

What you are now reading may appear to be a sales pitch—and, *yes,* I am also selling my services. But, more importantly, I am selling the idea of *coaching*. Of course, I would very much appreciate your business, but I believe what is most important is your getting a coach—regardless of your picking my company or not. Look at professional athletes. They all have coaches. These athletes are the very best at what they do, yet they know the value of a good coach. Every extremely successful person I know has at least one coach or mentor.

Find a Coach; Begin Your Search

Today, begin your search to find yourself a good coach, one who can help you reach your goals faster and more easily. You can search online, or you can seek one locally. One terrific benefit of coaching is that you can be coached by someone halfway across the planet via the Internet, email, or phone. Finding a great coach is not limited by geography.

I offer a *free* monthly teleconference call so that people can get a feel for me and my style. This is a great way to test the waters. For more information on our free monthly teleconference, visit:

www.donstaley.com/coaching/free-monthly-call

Would having a good coach accelerate your success and save you a great deal of pain and frustration? I believe the answer is YES. For more information on our coaching programs, visit:

www.donstaley.com/coaching

Get accountability. **Find a coach. Begin your search today. It will dramatically increase the speed and likelihood of your success.**

DAY TWENTY-SEVEN

Check off these boxes as you complete each task.

- ❑ Awareness part two
  - ❑ Become aware of your surroundings—others
  - ❑ Become aware of your surroundings—environment
  - ❑ Record your findings in your journal

AWARENESS PART 2

Day twenty-seven: For us to upgrade our lives, we must be aware of what we are being exposed to on a regular basis. Now is the time to become aware of the people around you. Keep tabs on the three to five people with whom you spend the most time. Their language patterns have an effect on you! It is important that you realize what they are consistently saying. What words are they using? Are they encouraging or discouraging you? What actions are they taking? What emotions are they expressing? You are keeping this type of dossier on the people you are around the most, because they will have a great impact on your success or lack of it. **We become like the people we are around.**

Become Aware of Your Surroundings—Others

Initially, take two weeks and track your next two to three interactions with those three to five individuals with whom you spend the most time.

Notice what they are saying, how often they say it, how they are behaving, and what emotions they are showing and expressing. You want to evaluate each person in your environment and ask yourself, "Do I want to become like this person?" As the saying goes, "Birds of a feather flock together." Be aware of your flock or environment and decide what you are going to do. If your current environment is not fertile, you can change it, leave it, or visit it less often.

Your associations with other people are not trivial matters. These people are having an impact on you, through repetition of time, and they are a part of your environment. I am emphasizing this again: we become like the people we hang around with the most (our environment). The good news is that you are becoming more aware of your environment and you can make adjustments if need be.

Over a long enough period of time, water, which is one of the softest substances on the planet, can carve out rock, one of the hardest substances. The Grand Canyon was formed by water running over rock and dirt. As soft as water is, if it consistently rubs against something as hard as rock, it will eventually wear it away. The softness of a friend or relative who is on the wrong track—based on your target—can wear away your dreams. Once you are aware of your environment, you can determine what you need to do to improve it.

Becoming aware is not done to judge our family, friends, or coworkers. Rather, it helps us become more mindful of what conditioning we are presently surrounded by. Everything in this universe is perfectly *imperfect*. No one is better than anyone else. We all originated from the same place. There may be things that are not to our taste or in alignment with where we are heading. However, we are not here to change them. We are here to live our lives and, if we choose, to improve ourselves. Therefore, we must understand our surroundings in order to improve upon them.

Become Aware of Your Surroundings—Environment

Take inventory of your environments, as discussed in chapter 16 on awareness. Refer back to this section to stimulate your thinking about what environments you currently spend your time in. Do your best to take an objective perspective of these environments. Use caution because it is from these environments that you have been "programmed." Be as objective as you can. Ask yourself, **"Is this environment helping me move toward my goals?"** Challenge those environments you are spending a good deal of time in each week and month.

Record Your Findings in Your Journal

When you are keeping the dossier on the people and environments that surround you, let judgment against people and organizations go. You may compare how their thoughts, emotions, and actions are either in alignment with your goals or not. If they are not, ask yourself, "Do I want to keep myself exposed to these kinds of thoughts, emotions, and behaviors?" If so, you may want to ask yourself, **"How much exposure is too much?"** This is a type of judgment, but not against the people or organizations. It is the *thoughts, emotions, and behaviors* that we are evaluating to determine whether they are aligned with where we are going or what we are choosing for ourselves.

To reiterate, one of my mentors said, **"You don't have to divorce people who are not in alignment with your new way of thinking. Just don't go as often or stay as long."**

DAY TWENTY-EIGHT

Check off these boxes as you complete each task.

- ❑ Checkup week four in review
  - ❑ Continue gratitude
  - ❑ Increase meditation practice
  - ❑ Mental martial arts process automatic negative thoughts (ANTs) review
  - ❑ Journal on five-day ANTs experience
  - ❑ Continue martial arts on ants
  - ❑ Create and begin listening to audio affirmations daily
  - ❑ Decide on final ideal body photo copy and post
  - ❑ Find a coach; begin search
  - ❑ Become aware of your surroundings—that of others and of your environment
  - ❑ Record your findings in your journal

CHECKUP WEEK FOUR IN REVIEW

Day twenty-eight: Wow! You did it! Four weeks of daily assignments. You are only days away from our goal of thirty days of programming. Also, you are taking decisive action and are committed to your vision. Bravo! My compliments to you! Look back at this past week and take any actions that may have slipped through the cracks. Tweak or upgrade any actions you would like to improve on.

Gratitude

Every day, as you awaken in the morning, feel grateful. Continue this throughout the day. Send out gratitude and appreciation for your life and all that is in it. "Thank you" can be your new mantra instead of any negative statements you may have said to yourself as you woke up.

Increase Meditation Practice

If you are not already there, begin to increase your meditation time to ten to fifteen minutes each day. Build your meditation muscle. **Namaste!** (This is an Indian or Nepalese greeting that means "bowing to you.")

ANTs Review; Journal on Five-Day Automatic Negative Thoughts Experience

Review any thoughts and feelings that you experienced while working with your ANTs during the five-day ANTs process.

Continue Mental Martial Arts on Your ANTs

Mentally, continue to stomp out any ANTs that occur by performing mental martial arts on them. "Thank you for serving me in the past, I no longer need you. I now choose this [insert your new *response/reply* thought pattern]."

Create and Begin Listening to Audio Affirmations Daily

Create an audio version of your affirmation sheet. Record yourself as you read your affirmation sheet aloud. Listen to your audio affirmations at least once a day; three is ideal. The more you listen, the better. Add *feelings of accomplishment* whenever you listen to your audio affirmations.

Decide on Your Final Ideal Body Photo; Copy and Post It

Finalize the ideal body photo and stick with it for the next sixty, ninety, 180, or however many days, weeks, or months it takes to reach your goal. This image is your ideal body. Copy and post your ideal body photo so that you will see it several times a day.

Find a Coach; Begin Search

Find yourself a good coach who will help you reach your goals faster and more easily. Search online or locally, but begin the hunt for your coach now. If you can get a referral, that is one of the best ways to find a good coach.

Become Aware of Your Surroundings—Others and Environment

Notice what the three to five individuals you spend the most time with are saying, how they are behaving, and what emotions they show and express. In what environments are you currently spending your time? What effect are they having on you? Evaluate these environments and decide how to handle any that are not conducive to your success.

Record Your Findings in Your Journal

Keep a dossier on the people and environments you are around. Ask yourself, "Do I want to continue to expose myself to these kinds of thoughts, emotions, and behaviors?" Record your feelings and findings in your journal.

DAY TWENTY-NINE

Check off these boxes as you complete each task.

- ❑ Increase meditation time duration

INCREASE MEDITATION TIME DURATION

Day twenty-nine: A week has passed since you last increased your meditation time. How is it going? This is a good time to evaluate your meditation practice and, depending on your intuitive feeling, increase the time or duration for each session. If you are ready, increase your daily meditation time to fifteen to twenty minutes. You are building a muscle, so only you know when it is time to add more weights.

DAY THIRTY

Check off these boxes as you complete each task.

- ❑ Accountability part four
- ❑ Find, join, or create a mastermind group

ACCOUNTABILITY PART 4

Day thirty: Today has the last assignment this month regarding accountability. Finding and joining a mastermind group is one of the last major assignments of this thirty-day program. The mastermind group can be another helpful tool to speed your success. If you don't find what you are looking for, then create your own mastermind group.

Find, Join, or Create a Mastermind Group

The next action item is to join, form, or start a mastermind group of like-minded individuals who are striving for a similar goal. Ideally, these people will be familiar with the concepts in this book. They will also encourage and push you to the success you are seeking, and in exchange, you will push and encourage them.

With the assistance of technology these days, there are many options for helping to form a mastermind group. Here is a list of several ideas:

1. Attend seminars and conferences, and seek out people to form a group. *Because I think this is so valuable,* at all of *our* live events going forward, we allocate time specifically for masterminding.

2. Start an online mastermind group at websites such as:

- Facebook.com
- Google.com
- Yahoo.com
- Meetup.com
- YouTube.com
- LinkedIn.com
- Twitter.com

3. There are many other social networking websites you can find when you do a search. You can also do a search on this book title to see if there are any groups you can join.

4. You can start a book club focused on this book by posting on forums and blogs online. You can visit such websites as Amazon.com and BarnesandNoble.com, as well as Borders.com, and you can read writer reviews of this book. Furthermore, contact others who have written reviews on this book to see if they would be interested in joining a mastermind group.

5. Find several friends who are interested in creating their ideal bodies, buy each of them this book (or encourage them to invest in copies of their own), and form your own book club/mastermind group. Then you can all go through this book together. There is power in the mastermind group.

DAY THIRTY-ONE

Check off these boxes as you complete each task.

- ❑ Understanding
- ❑ Life continues; take the next step

UNDERSTANDING

Day thirty-one: The next step is to continue to **increase your understanding**. This step is very important in the overall scheme of things. Initially, it can be put off for thirty to ninety days, until you get the momentum going and are more comfortable with the reconditioning process. I suggest you continue with the reprogramming process until you reach your goals. When all of your reconditioning actions become habits, I encourage you to continue to learn and grow.

We increase our understanding every day without taking any conscious action. However, what I am talking about is taking steps consciously to learn and grow. Reading, studying, and going to seminars and conferences are excellent ways to increase your understanding.

Only entertain concepts and ideas that are in alignment with those in this book. If you expose yourself to an environment that belittles these ideas or contradicts these thoughts, you'll be undermining your belief in the process and your chances of success. If you believe something, you'll do it. If you don't believe, you will not spend your energy, and thus you won't accomplish your goals. It is important to keep the faith. Be very careful to whom you subject yourself.

We all know the power of a magnifying glass and that of a laser. **Stay focused. Stay on track. You have that power, so keep it for yourself. Avoid giving it away and continue to make empowering decisions.**

After two or three months—or whenever you believe you are ready—read other related materials on the same subject pertaining to mindset, the subconscious mind, and habits. Ideally, you will read and study this book three times, spending about thirty continuous days doing so each time. Constant and perpetual improvement will increase your understanding tremendously. I hope you have committed yourself to continual and lasting self-improvement. Have you done so?

Whether you realize it or not, you have already accomplished great things, and you will do even greater things. Every one of us is changing the world in one way or another. Every thought, feeling, and action you take has a consequence. The underlying questions are: 1) What kind of effect are you choosing to create in this world? 2) What action is required to do that? 3) What mark do you choose to leave?

There will never, in the entire universe, ever be anyone exactly like you again! This is *your time*. What are you going to do with it?

"The shortest and surest way to live with honor in the world is to be in reality what we would appear to be; and if we observe, we shall find, that all human virtues increase and strengthen themselves by the practice of them."

—Socrates

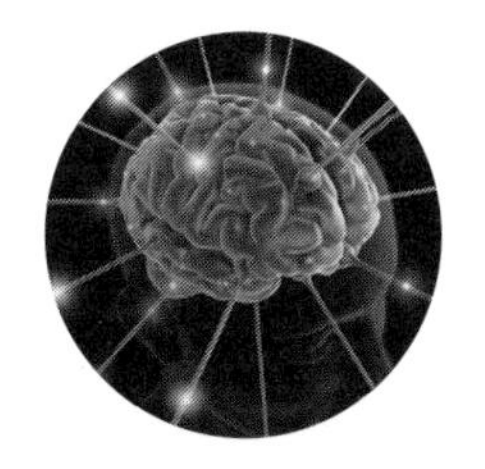

CONCLUSION

Life Continues: Take The Next Step

Where do you go from here? Every time you write down your goals in the morning, I recommend that you celebrate. Praise and reward yourself for taking this new action. The same action will be easier to take the next time, because rewarding yourself makes taking the action a positive event. In the beginning, even a move toward taking an action is cause for some celebration or a small reward. The greater the progress, the bigger the reward and celebration will be.

We are creating new neural nets or brain cells linked together. When we add emotion, it makes the connection stronger. Remember that with emotions, certain proteins are released at the synaptic gaps, thus making the connections "wire together." Essentially, this path becomes easier to travel, and eventually, it becomes the path of least resistance. Celebrate your efforts, successes, and even your failures. John C. Maxwell wrote a book titled *Failing Forward*. The more you fail, the more you learn, which ultimately brings you to your goal. Remember to fail up, or forward.

I believe that I have done my part to assist you along your path. For over twenty years, I endured frustration and defeat before I eventually found the solution. I put forth my best effort to write this book, and it is now up to you. **You have a decision to make. What are you going to do with this information?** Your conditioning may have been an unknown factor before you read this book, but now you know. Even more important, **now you know how to change your conditioning and improve your life.** Will you? Will you take action? I can only hope you do. I know this approach works because these are the same ideas that helped me and countless others change our lives. Where I am now compared to where I was before I applied these ideas is as different as night is to day! Now I can see clearly!

I have spelled out exactly what to do, and I have gone beyond that. I have laid out an action plan to follow. You now know exactly what actions to take and when. Now, it is up to you. If you would like to take what you learned further with additional support from me—perhaps, in one of our coaching or mentoring programs—contact us to check for availability.

Here is something profound to understand: there is no wrong decision. If you decide not to take this next step to consciously move your life forward, it is OK. The universe operates perfectly whether we see it or not. We are all evolving and moving forward in one conscious evolution, regardless of our conscious intention to increase our understanding. Even by accident, we manage to progress.

My intention is to get this book into the hands of those who are attracting this information and will consciously take control. **This book is for those who choose more, who desire to live in greater abundance.** Abundance is available for us all. If you've read this far, my guess is that you have made a decision to experience more of life. When you take these ideas, read them, understand them, internalize them, and, most importantly, effectively apply them in your life, you will reap rewards beyond your current imagination. True learning takes place when you *apply* these ideas. I believe that you have this book in your hands for a reason. It is not an accident, because there are no accidents.

What you desire will ultimately affect millions of people. In fact, it will affect everyone and everything. You may not be able to see it or grasp it with your five senses, but perhaps with your new understanding, you will realize this to be true. When you examine what the world looks like after the accomplishment of your desire through a quantum physics perspective, you know it is true. **This is the fork in the road. Either you can take the path most others take, which is actually harder, or you can take the path that requires some conscious effort but offers an immense payoff. What are you going to do?**

If you have seen the hit movie *The Matrix*, you may remember the main character, Neo. Played by Keanu Reeves, he *learns* about The Matrix. However, in order to *experience* the matrix, he has to take the red pill. If he takes the blue pill, he goes back to living in ignorance and won't know any difference. If he takes the red pill, he has the opportunity to learn how far the rabbit hole goes. In the scene in which Neo is considering taking the red pill and Morpheus is guiding him, Morpheus says to Neo, **"All I am offering you is the truth."**

Morpheus also said to Neo, **"I can only show you the door; you have to walk through it."**

There are a lot of great hidden messages in that movie series. In this book is a truth as I have experienced it. Here is a door! It is now up to you to decide if you are going to walk through it. Which pill are you going to take? The red pill requires that you reread, study, and apply the ideas in this book, while taking the blue pill means that you will put the book down and do nothing with it. Remember, I am offering you a truth. Will you reach out for it? Will you embrace it?

If you ever need help along this path, I am here, like an excited parent waiting for his young child to take his or her first step. Here is what I say to you: "You can do it, and I love you."

The end of this book is a new BEGINNING for your new life.

Enjoy the journey!

APPENDIX 1

Word Translator from Normal/Negative to Empowering

Negative	Positive	Sentence
Can't	I can, Still open for a solution, In the process	I am in the process of finding a solution.
Should	Next time I will	Next time I will do better.
Try	I will do my best, Nice effort	I will put forth my best effort.
Want	Choose	I choose to be fit and healthy.
Problem	Challenge	This is only a challenge, and it can be solved.

Links

Link for bonus three-month free weekly email coaching program: www.donstaley.com/fitmindbook

Link for free monthly group preview calls: www.donstaley.com/coaching/free-monthly-call

Link for advanced coaching/mentoring: www.donstaley.com/coaching

APPENDIX 2

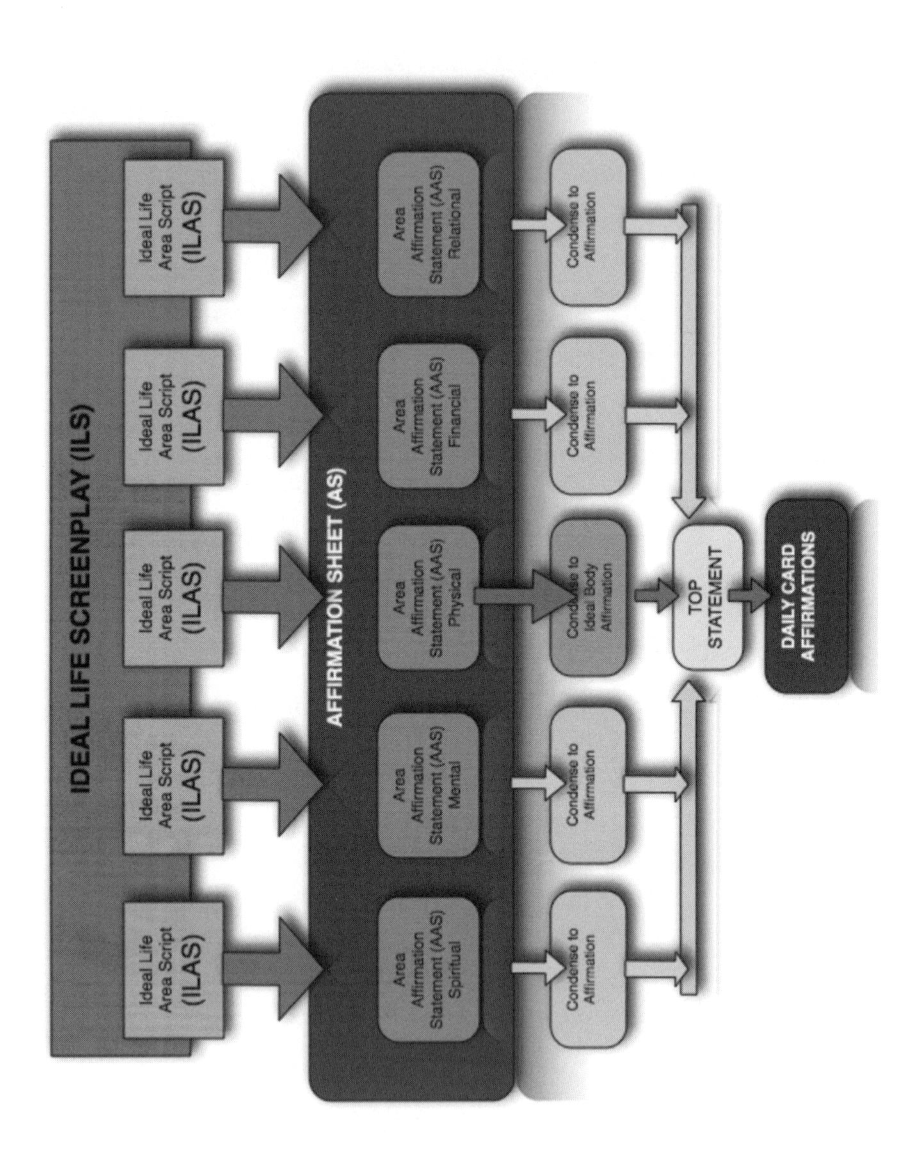
IDEAL LIFE SCREENPLAY (ILS)
Ideal Life Area Script (ILAS)
Ideal Life Area Script (ILAS)
Ideal Life Area Script (ILAS)
Ideal Life Area Script (ILAS)
Ideal Life Area Script (ILAS)
AFFIRMATION SHEET (AS)
Area Affirmation Statement (AAS) Spiritual
Area Affirmation Statement (AAS) Mental
Area Affirmation Statement (AAS) Physical
Area Affirmation Statement (AAS) Financial
Area Affirmation Statement (AAS) Relational
Condense to Affirmation
Condense to Affirmation
Condense to Ideal Body Affirmation
Condense to Affirmation
Condense to Affirmation
TOP STATEMENT
DAILY CARD AFFIRMATIONS

APPENDIX 3

Superstar Success Compass

APPENDIX 4

Accountability and Commitment

Agreement #1 (FITNESS)

On this ______ day of________in the year 20____, I _________________, do enter into this contract willingly and with full knowledge of what is expected of me by me. I enter into this contract to commit myself to being physically fit by creating permanent fitness habits through reconditioning my mind with the reprogramming process.

My plan of action is this:
I reserve a minimum of 30–60 minutes*, seven days a week during the next 90 days for the mental reprogramming (re-training) process.

1. I follow the coaching program laid out by Don Staley in his book *FIT MIND, FIT BODY.*

2. I follow all action steps in the 30-day action plan in the book *FIT MIND, FIT BODY,* including the four parts of the reprogramming process.

3. I take action on a daily basis with my action goals to accomplish my target of

   ____

4. On a daily basis, I reward myself for my successful efforts with:

   ____

5. On a weekly basis, I reward myself for my successful efforts with:

   ____

6. When I have accomplished my objective of ________________, I shall take my family _____________ (insert your preference [picnic, camping, vacation, etc.]) and spend a day or two relaxing—complete with a picnic lunch of my favorite foods. I will take pictures, rejoice in my favorite picnic place and celebrate my success.

7. By doing these things, I plan to have reached my ideal weight of ________ by ______Day, ______Month, 20______.

8. By ____Day, ______Month, 20_____, I will begin phase two of my fitness program.

I realize the importance of each person to whom I have sent a copy of this contract, and I call upon each one to police my heartfelt efforts in whatever loving way he or she chooses. If I am caught falling behind on any of the goals listed above and their corresponding deadlines, I hereby promise to treat the detector—that person who receives an official copy of this contract—to a dinner at his or her favorite restaurant.

______________________________   __________________

Signed   *Date*

*In the beginning it may be 10–15 minutes.

Email/mail five copies to your accountability partners. Email one copy to me at: don@donstaley.com. Print, sign, and keep a copy for yourself.

APPENDIX 5

Accountability and Commitment

Agreement #2 (GENERAL)

On this _______ day of _________________ in the year _____________,

I, _____________________________, do enter into this contract willingly and with full knowledge of what is expected of me by me. I write this contract to commit myself to: ______________________________.

The ability to live up to this commitment is already inside of me.

I complete this task by__________ of the year __________.

I do understand the necessity of this contract's binding me to a commitment of taking this (these) action(s) on a daily basis, every day, for the next 90 days:

Reprogramming: ____.

Action goal: ____.

I reserve __________________ (minutes, hours) daily, seven days a week, to the reprogramming process for the next 90 days.

I remove all distractions, I set boundaries for those near and dear to me and ask them to respect those boundaries so that I may have uninterrupted time.

I post my results on a bulletin board on the wall above my desk (or prominent area).

I make a list of my ideal life and all I desire to have, do, and become. I list them into daily and weekly actions.

On a daily basis, I reward myself with a _________________________.

When I have accomplished ______________, I shall treat myself (and my spouse and children) to a full-course, luxury dinner at a nice restaurant.

When I have finished___________, I shall travel to_______________ and spend the day, complete with a picnic lunch of my favorite foods. I take pictures and rejoice in my favorite place. I take my children if possible.

If any one of my accountability partners catches me falling behind on any of the goals listed above and their corresponding deadlines,I hereby promise to treat the detector—that person who receives an official copy of this contract—to a dinner at his or her favorite restaurant.

I gladly, willingly, and most excitedly sign this contract.

______________________________ ____________________

Signed *Date*

Email/mail five copies to your accountability partners. Email one copy to me at: don@donstaley.com. Print, sign, and keep a copy for yourself.

Index

About the Author

After twenty-plus years of "trying" to maintain a consistent physical fitness program and failing, Don Staley, like many others, was met with only temporary and sporadic success. Even after twenty years of personal development using books, audio, and seminars—and even though he was motivated—he still lacked a few key insights to be consistent. Frustrated and discouraged, he almost gave up on staying fit. Finally, his persistent digging unearthed a number of critical gems that most speakers and gurus do NOT teach.

Before learning these ideas, Don's longest fitness program lasted only a few months. However, when he put these gems together, he was able to begin a highly successful physical fitness program and remain on it every day for over four years—and he is still going strong!

Don says that the success he experienced has nothing to do with exercise, gadgets, or fad diets. Instead, it has everything to do with the proper mindset. He now teaches these empowering ideas so that others can fulfill their dreams of creating the ideal, fit body. Don Staley helps people transform their lives by revolutionizing their habits.

Don Staley is a professional speaker, coach/mentor and the author of five books, including Fit Mind, Fit Body, in which he shares a new transformational formula to revolutionize your fitness habits. Don has authored four other books and they are Every Day Counts, New Year's Resolutions that Stick, Retrain Your Mind, and A Quick Guide of 25 Healthier Snack Alternatives to Fast Food.

He also co-authored two additional books: The Power of Mentorship Finding Your Passion and The Power of Mentorship The Mastermind Group with Bob Proctor, Brian Tracy and Zig Ziglar.

His true passion is speaking, coaching, teaching, and inspiring individuals, companies, and organizations to realize their true potential—not through hype or motivation, but by the latest research in neuroscience and quantum physics.

Don Staley is married to his wife, Angie, and they have two wonderful children, Nicholas and Reese.

Books By Don Staley

The Power of Mentorship Finding Your Passion (co-author)	$19.95
The Power of Mentorship and The Mastermind Group (co-author)	$19.95
Fit Mind, Fit Body: How to Achieve Your Ideal Body and Keep it FOREVER by Putting Your Motivation on Autopilot!	$24.95
Every Day Counts: The Simple (and Effective) Way To Achieve Outrageously Big Goals	$14.95
New Years Resolutions That Stick: How To Make Life-Changing Resolutions That Work For You...Every Single Year!	$14.95
Retrain Your Mind: To Get in The Best Shape Of Your Life	$14.95
A Quick Guide of 25 Healthier Snack Alternatives to Fast Food	$12.95

Special Quantity Discounts	
20–25 Books	$18 each
26–99 Books	$16 each
100–499 Books	$14 each
500–999 Books	$12 each
+1000 Books	call for details

For more information about hiring Don Staley for coaching/mentoring or speaking, contact:

1-800-913-8517

or visit:

www.donstaley.com